Self-H
Recovery

Exploring The Evidence

Bruce Wallace

chipmunkapublishing
the mental health publisher

Published by
Chipmunkapublishing
United Kingdom

http://www.chipmunkapublishing.com

ISBN   978-1-78382-160-0

Chipmunkapublishing gratefully acknowledge the support of Arts Council England.

CHAPTERS

STORIES

CHAPTER CONTRIBUTORS

'J':
'J' is a teacher in mainstream primary education. She currently lives in Scotland and is in her 30s. 'J' is comfortable with others knowing about her personal experience regarding self-harm in the hope that it can help others. It is out of respect for her friends   and   family that she wishes to remain anonymous.

Pras Ramluggun:
Dr. Pras Ramluggun is a mental health lecturer at the University Campus Suffolk and Kings College London. He has extensive experience and a comprehensive working knowledge of the organisation and delivery of forensic mental health services. He completed his PhD with the University of East Anglia in June 2012 comparing attitudinal dimensions to self-harm and the seasonal variation of this phenomenon in prison. His interests are in legal and ethical practice in the field of mental health especially in the custodial setting. While holding the post of clinical Lead/Advisor in the Norfolk Prison Cluster he has implemented and led an innovative service to address the primary mental health needs of prisoners.

Amy Chandler:
Dr. Amy Chandler is a sociologist specialising in mental health (particularly self-harm/suicide), health services research, and qualitative, life-story methods. Theoretically she is interested in the importance of bodies to understanding 'lived experience'; the impact of communication (in the broadest sense) on mental health and family life; the ways in which embodied practices become medicalised; how health related practices are negotiated in medical and other settings. Her doctoral research on self-harm was completed in 2010. The research comprised a sociological analysis of self-injury, focusing on embodied aspects of the behaviour.

Naomi Salisbury:
Naomi Salisbury has personal experience of using self-harm and has spent a lot of time trying to make sense of it for herself and other people. In her work life she has run collective advocacy projects on personality disorder and psychosis at CAPS Advocacy (www.capsadvocacy.org); developed and delivered training on the experiences of personality disorder diagnosis and self-harm; made a short film about dissociation and Borderline Personality Disorder and exhibited work in this area in the Scottish Mental Health Arts and Film Festival. She now runs a helpline for women affected by

self-injury at Self-Injury Support (formerly Bristol Crisis Service for Women) (www.selfinjurysupport.org.uk.)

Maria Naranjo:
Maria trained as a Psychotherapist in Spain. She obtained an MSc in Cognitive Science from Edinburgh University. Maria has worked in the field of Mental Health in Scotland for over a decade. She set up Mind's Well in 2011 as a social enterprise. In her previous position in a National Charity she worked as Self Harm Co-ordinator and gained valuable experience and knowledge of the issues affecting people who engage in self-harming behaviours and those who look after them, professionally or personally. Furthermore, she provided managerial, developmental and strategic support to several projects.

Lora Coyle:
Lora Coyle has been volunteering with the organisation since Mind's Well started in September 2011.
Lora is 28 and has been using self-harm for 14 years. Now she shares her experience in our workshops to educate people about self-harm related issues and to raise awareness. Lora is an integral part in the delivery of our self-harm courses.

Bruce Wallace
Bruce Wallace is a visiting lecturer at the University of Bedfordshire. Prior to semi-retirement he was a senior lecturer in mental health and learning disabilities at the same university. He originally trained as a mental health nurse and had a range of practice experience before becoming a nursing tutor and then university lecturer. He has facilitated a specialist education module on suicide and self-harming behaviours and has run workshops exploring a range of issues related to the subject of self-harm. He has previously published a book on the topic entitled: *Self-harm/injury: An exploration of attitudes and issues from literature and personal stories.*

Glossary of abbreviations used in the book:

ACCT	The Assessment, Care and Custody and Teamwork document
CAMHS	Child and Adolescent Mental Health Services
CAPS	The Consultation and Advocacy Promotion Service
CBT	Cognitive Behaviour Therapy (A psychosocial approach; sometimes referred to as 'talking therapy')
CPN	Community Psychiatric Nurse (now usually referred to as a Community Mental Health Nurse)
DBT	Dialectical Behaviour Therapy (Another psychosocial approach; used frequently for individuals diagnosed with a Borderline Personality Disorder)
DH	Department of Health
GCSE	General Certificate of Secondary Education
GP	General Practitioner
HIT	term historically used to indicate a file sent to a browser by a web server. Each file is a hit.
HMP	Her Majesty's Prison
HSE	Health Service Executive (Ireland)
MBA	Masters in Business Administration
NSSI	Non-Suicidal Self-Injury
NSW CAG	New South Wales Consumer Advisory Group
ODs	Overdoses
WHO	World Health Organisation

Bruce Wallace

Acknowledgements:

This book has only been made possible through the support demonstrated by a range of individuals who have given of their time, experience and expertise. The process has slowly gathered momentum and grown from an idea finally into a reality. The gradual nature of the development has at times been a little frustrating for someone who initially started off planning a rapid start to finish process, namely myself!

I can now finally apologize to those individuals who have been regularly emailed regarding 'progress' on their identified contributions. As someone who is now retired and working occasionally on a visiting lecturer basis, it has been a little difficult to appreciate the sacrifice in terms of time and effort needed, that people have had to make to provide the contributions they have to the book. The people mentioned in the following paragraphs have not been identified in any order of priority but all have been instrumental in helping to transfer an idea for a book into the finished product.

A special mention for the following: Merrick, Nina, Mary, Wedge and Jules for taking the time to identify contacts with agencies and individuals. Through their direct working relationships they were in a unique position to be able to offer a range of names and/or contacts, obviously subject to those identified agreeing. This has helped me to access a much wider range of individuals and groups than I could possibly have achieved on my own.

Thank you to Karen and Nicky for providing some interesting ideas during a number of telephone and email conversations. Although it was not possible for you to offer specific contributions (in terms of written input) due to a range of commitments your advice was appreciated and helped to shape some of the ideas that are reflected in elements of the book.

Thank you to Janine, Denise and Suzanne for taking the time and providing the expertise to proof a large part of the work, identifying errors and issues and ensuring that the work takes on greater clarity. Again an appreciation of the time that you have donated against the background of a very busy schedule is not forgotten.

It is of immense help when a number of people with a wide range of knowledge and experience, together with a limited timeframe give both in the way of direct contribution. Your willingness to become involved, together with the recognition of the time and effort that would then be required, is fully acknowledged and appreciated. To commit to supporting an idea and then continuing to demonstrate that commitment by submitting outlines, drafts and then updated drafts on an ongoing basis is worthy of this recognition. To Amy, Pras, Maria, Lora, Naomi, and 'J', a very special thank you for giving both your time and invaluable input.

To those individuals who were prepared to trust me sufficiently to offer their personal experiences related to self-harm and the idea of recovery as part of this project, a special thank you. The writers of the stories may be anonymous to the reader but this is to ensure that the confidentiality of each individual is respected and maintained. It is important to appreciate that individuals who have been contacted, usually via a local contact, group or individual, are then prepared to share a very private part of their life and experiences with a total stranger.

Some email conversations did take place where individuals wanted to clarify what my plans were or other issues such as objectives, requirements and schedule but again through the modern world of technology. This may assist anonymity to a degree at one level but also identifies the need for trust and respect to exist to enable an end product to become possible. It is not forgotten that some of you have 'identified' yourselves during this process and I can only thank you for that degree of trust being shown. It is through your willingness to provide your experiences that others can gain a valuable insight into the 'world' of self-harm, the idea of recovery, and how it directly affects individuals from a wide range of areas and ages.

Finally, last but not least the recognition of the sacrifices that my wife and family have had to make; notably in terms of time and my not infrequent absences regularly spent on the computer. Requests for ideas that might help to 'shape' the book, its content, and focus were met with patience and responses that were both constructive and positive. I am fortunate to be surrounded by a family who are both knowledgeable and sufficiently experienced to ensure that any advice asked for and received is balanced, appropriate and constructive. To my family - thank you.

Content	**Page**

Content ... **Page**

INTRODUCTION

Self-harm is an aspect of so many peoples' lives that it attracts a range of attention that varies between the sympathetic at one extreme to the accusatory at the other. Individuals who self-harm do not necessarily 'choose' this process to deal with whatever has created a specific need in their current situation. Unfortunately this interpretation is not always shared by all of those who come into contact with someone who has self-harmed. Therein exists one of the major challenges as this can result in difficulties for the individual when seeking help as in:

- *If I self-harm and want to consider a potential alternative that frightens me less; offers me a less painful or risk orientated way of dealing with my distress or need, who do I confide in or ask for help or support?*

When I first became aware of self-harm, it was a way in which some people appeared to either deal with a crisis in their lives or it appeared to be utilized to overcome past or present traumas. I became interested partly due to my limited knowledge and understanding and partly due to taking on the responsibility for facilitating an undergraduate module at my university entitled 'suicide and self-harming behaviour'. I therefore wanted to try and understand the two topics more and in particular attempt to understand what motivated some individuals to need to self-harm. I considered this a first step in attempting to explore what might be offered as an alternative to this person to reduce the possibility of the need to self-harm and ways in which injury or even death might be avoided. An exploration of what self-harm was and what it meant to people who had direct experience formed the basis of the first book that I undertook in this area.

During this process one of the elements that occasionally arose but did not adequately get covered was that of the concept of 'recovery'. Some considerations arose but due to the focus were not addressed to any significant degree. They are clarified in the following bullet points:

- Do people who are self-harming recover?
- Is there some process that occurs whereby the person moves from a point where self-harm is an integral part of their lives to one where it becomes less of a central 'character'?
- Indeed is there a point where self-harm no longer has a significant place and the person moves on with their life?

My own professional background is in mental health nursing and it consisted initially of working in mental health practice in a variety of settings. The practice element of my experience took place during the late nineteen sixties and early seventies when self-harm was largely 'invisible' to many mental health nurses. Individuals who self-harmed but were considered not to have attempted suicide were frequently labelled as 'attention seeking' with little attempt to explore why this behaviour was happening. I later moved into nursing education and became involved in preparing students for entry to the nursing register or with practitioners who already had experience and/or qualifications in the field of mental health. As someone who worked within a variety of 'professional' mental health environments for most of my working life the process model learned and applied was one that generally helped to understand what was happening in someone's life; i.e.

- Person functions apparently normally with life and the various challenges that arise
- Situation changes either suddenly or gradually and the person's ability to deal with situations and their role becomes compromised
- The individual, their family, friends, and/or colleagues identify a concern and ask/require help and/or support
- The individual is helped and/or supported by 'specialist' services to enable them to return to or move towards a situation whereby they can resume a 'normal' life (i.e. recover).

Unfortunately the above scenario does not really incorporate a situation within which people engage in behaviour that results in harm and/or injury to themselves (other than attempted suicide). It is also complicated in as much as it may or may not include mental health problems. The current statistics in this country (United Kingdom) suggest that accident and emergency departments will record somewhere in the region of 300,000 attendances annually where individuals have self-harmed. Despite the increasing amount of literature now available on the subject of self-harm there is an acknowledgement that mainstream services such as health care still struggle with individuals who present having self-harmed in terms of appropriate support and planned interventions.

The various guidelines developed since those first introduced by NICE (2004) all generally support the idea of a person-centred process where each individual is treated with dignity and respect and offered privacy with the opportunity to talk about their needs as appropriate within a non-judgmental environment. The reality is less clear and research indicates that the individual's experience can be varied depending on who they encounter and where. One of the area's most frequently visited by individuals seeking help and/or support having self-harmed is the nearest accident and emergency department (A&E) of their local hospital. Given the recent acknowledgement that there is an awareness of the significant pressure on A&E departments, the opportunity for staff working in these to provide the time to engage effectively with individuals is likely to be compromised. This is particularly pertinent when it comes to being able to provide time to listen to what the individual who has self-harmed may wish to discuss regarding their circumstances.

Notwithstanding comments made previously that acknowledge the varied experiences that exist, it is important to consider that there is life beyond self-harm and this is the main thrust of the book. The choice of recovery as a construct has attracted a variety of responses and this identifies the way in which this term is viewed both within the mental health 'professional' community and by other agencies, organisations and individuals. Those who have direct experience of accessing services may contain individuals who believe it is rather less positive in its interpretation and more aligned to expectations than reality.

In a bid to represent a broad range of experiences and therefore views I initially contacted individuals, organisations and agencies in a bid to encourage responses that would explore the concept of self-harm and recovery and then consider whether this had any value. The chapters and stories provided bear witness to the complexity that emerged when attempting to investigate what at first appeared to be a relatively straightforward process, at least to me! It is also important to note that an awareness of the value of stories has been balanced with the responsibility to ensure that they are utilized for the benefit of those who provided them and not for any organizational validation as stated in an article by Costa et al (2012) exploring the possible use *'by the psychiatric system to bolster research, education and fundraising events'. (p85)*

References:

Costa L., Voronka J., Landry D., Reid J., McFarlane B., Reville D., and Church K. (2012), Recovering our Stories: A Small Act of Resistance, Studies in Social Justice, Volume 6, Issue 1, pp.85-101

NICE. (2004), Self-harm: The short-term physical and psychological management and secondary prevention of self-harm in primary and secondary care, London, National Institute for Clinical Excellence

Chapter 1
RECOVERY IN THE CONTEXT OF SELF-HARM
Bruce Wallace

Within this chapter we will explore some of the many variations related to the concept of recovery and its meaning. This is especially important if we are to try and consider its relationship in the context of self-harm. Whether people support or oppose the current perceived importance of recovery in mental health care is really incidental because there is a marked emphasis currently placed on including it within any plan of care for a person with mental health problems. Given that self-harming behaviour is frequently associated with mental health problems (rightly or wrongly) within the literature and care services, the concept of recovery is therefore relevant.

It is important to indicate that although there are many different facets to recovery as a concept, it is outside the remit of this chapter and indeed this book to look beyond the relationship between recovery and self-harm that exists or is perceived to exist. To enable this to have some degree of credibility, the views and opinions of a range of practitioners, individuals and others are reflected in some of the literature identified, incorporated and utilized within this chapter. This will allow the reader the opportunity to formulate some thoughts regarding the two constructs (i.e. Recovery; Self-Harm) and then any relationship that may appear to exist between them.

The subject of self-harm itself has attracted a significant degree of attention over the past couple of decades in particular and is now seen by many as an issue that challenges many of the present day services (e.g. health, social, educational) both in terms of response and planned support and/or interventions. Although self-harm is not a new concept it is only in more recent times that it appears to have started to attract markedly more attention through an increase in the amount of literature that has appeared both within public and professional domains.

The emergence of a range of voluntary agencies and services that have come into being specifically to extend the range of information, advice and support available to individuals who self-harm is another consideration when it comes to a greater awareness of the subject. The range of material now available has focused more attention on the subject of self-harm with much of it exploring a number of diverse issues including:

- What does self-harm mean and why does it occur?
- Terminology used to identify the phenomenon
- Potential sub-divisions within the term self-harm which is sometimes referred to as an 'umbrella' term
- How many people may be self-harming
- Who self-harms?
- Possible/potential relationship(s) between self-harm and suicide
- Relationships between self-harm and mental health problems
- Interventions and strategies that may support individuals and/or reduce the incidence of self-harming behaviour.

Despite self-harm being closely associated with mental health problems and therefore mental health services and ideologies, one aspect that has attracted less attention within the majority of this literature is that of the idea of recovery and how it might apply or be applied to people who self-harm. Where interventions are discussed they tend to focus on issues such as mental health problems that have been identified and then how a reduction of either the frequency or severity (or both) of the self-harming behaviour may be achieved. An essential acknowledgement here is that the self-harming behaviour and mental health problem are not necessarily related although they may be occurring simultaneously. It is important to take into consideration that not all individuals who self-harm have identified mental health problems and therefore may perceive mental health service intervention as inappropriate for both them and any needs that they determine they may have.

The concept of recovery, particularly from a mental health perspective, appears to sit less comfortably within this topic area than within what might be described as mainstream mental health care. Within the arena of mental health the idea of recovery has tended to be perceived as one that may take on a number of different meanings as explored within the following section.

Recovery:
Within the next section a number of differing interpretations (some overlapping) are identified and outlined for consideration. They include the idea of an individual who may be helped by:

A). A specific service directly (e.g. *assessment, diagnosis, admission, treatment, professional input/support, group support, counselling/therapy) * *not all of these may necessarily apply to any one individual or be provided by a single agency/service.*

B).   The experience associated with their illness/condition and how it has impacted on their life. The individual takes 'control' of any agenda that may be of value to assist them in the management of their life accessing and/or utilizing support as they perceive appropriate.

C).   Proactive or Preventative means avoiding the consequence that may arise (as in A). Here recovery is based on a retrospective idea that once identified (e.g. through research, experience), issues that have a significant influence on an individual's wellbeing can be ameliorated. This occurs through programmes that focus on providing individuals and/or groups with the necessary help, support, guidance and education intended to reduce the risk of an individual developing issues that may result in the need for later intervention of a more significant nature (e.g. illness/condition). Examples include school/youth incentives. An awareness of an increasing incidence of self-harming behaviour in older people is another example of evidence (Packer et al, 2012) alerting services to a situation that needs consideration. When encountering individuals who are older than those cited in much of the literature and research related to self-harm, there is a suggestion that the role of the General Practitioner (GP) is of particular importance. The GP is also identified (Sinclair & Green 2005) as a familiar figure (along with school counsellors) that may be considered more 'user friendly' for young people than many other professionals encountered. These people will generally be strangers to the individual and are most likely to be in contact within tertiary settings such as a hospital environment.

When considering models related to the concept of recovery a number exist but may (considering the examples offered) be seen as comprising of the following, although close inspection may establish the presence of overlaps:

1. 'TRADITIONAL' RECOVERY (sometimes referred to as the Medical Model):

- Identification of an illness/condition that attracts a diagnostic label
- Introduction of a treatment/intervention regime based on the diagnosis
- Expectation of the individual 'recovering' from the illness or acute episode of the illness/condition

2. MAINTENANCE MODEL:

- Identification of significant challenges in treating the diagnosed condition effectively enough to enable the individual to resume independent living, working and/or socializing
- Focus placed on stabilizing or reducing the impact of the condition on the individual usually through maintenance (e.g. medication) or other interventions that aid the individual (maybe within a residential environment)
- Expectation is that 'recovery' will be based on a gradual improvement in the individual's capacity to move towards a less dependent need for professional support/intervention

3. RECOVERY MODEL (based frequently on a range of personal contributions by service users):

- Awareness and understanding of own illness/condition
- Assuming control/responsibility for own life
- Establishing hope for the future
- Working with 'specialists' (as required) on an equal basis

Within the large body of literature available there has been an ongoing debate of the recovery phenomena for the best part of the last four decades. This frequently revolved around a model based heavily on the individual who, through their personal experience of a mental health problem, has emerged as an 'expert by experience', and has at some point challenged the mainstream organisations charged with providing services in mental health. Although self-harm is not mentioned in the article by Davidson (2005) the opening statement could be seen to relate to some individuals who self-harm:

'Many of the skills required to manage their lives and their emotional distress can be acquired once people begin to believe in their own capacity to recover, to develop self-belief'.

One of the widely cited pieces of work exploring this approach to recovery is that of Anthony (1993) who states:

'Professionals do not hold the key to recovery; consumers do. The task of professionals is to facilitate recovery. Recovery may be facilitated by the consumer's natural support system. After all, if recovery is a common human condition experienced by us all, then people who are in touch with their own recovery can help others through the process. Self-help groups, families, and friends are the best examples of this phenomenon'. (p15)

There has been a degree of simplification within some debates where a Medical versus Recovery Model emerges implying that the two are separate entities and may even be diametrically opposed. The medical model is perceived by some to be where the professionals control what happens to the service user compared to the recovery model where the emphasis is on the service user taking more control over their destiny with less dependence on the professionals who are accessed by the service user as needed.

This tends to overlook the myriad of professional groups involved including therapists and counsellors who are not usually perceived to be part of the medical model in the roles that they are engaged in. Others are a little more conciliatory in their interpretation. Some examples from the literature have been identified and included below to enable the reader to gauge the diversity of opinion that pervades this topic. One way of looking at the distinction is succinctly stated by NSW CAG as:

- The medical model drives from the clinical view of recovery; recovery is objective and understood to be a return to a former state of health. Outcomes include reduced symptomatology, hospitalization and medication use
- The personal view of recovery is driven by people's lived, subjective experiences of mental illness and recovery, and challenges the notion of permanent mental illness. Outcomes include empowerment, hope, choice, self-defined goals, healing, wellbeing and control of symptoms. (NSW CAG, 2009)

It should also be noted that there are those who consider that the approach represented by the medical model has been somewhat distorted as indicated previously and that it is sometimes viewed as a competing concept. It is indicated in some of the available literature that good practice in medicine incorporates a number of key components of the recovery approach, including hope, optimism and empowerment (Mountain & Shah, 2008). Unfortunately not all practice is perceived as positive by either practitioners or those seeking help and support. Kemp (2009) explores two primary approaches towards young people identifying the dichotomy that may exist as:

1. Those who view their task as primarily to control, manage and stop the behaviour (frequently hospital services)

2. Those who view their task as primarily to support the young person in their daily lives, in expressing their difficult emotions (p17)

It might be beginning to dawn on the reader by now that attempting to explain recovery as a singular and concrete construct is very difficult given the myriad of interpretations and meanings conveyed. A further conceptualization is that put forward in Barber's (2012) article of three 'types' of recovery, including:

a. Cure, or remission of the illness
b. Illness management, symptom control and long-term monitoring
c. Personal recovery, functioning at one's best.

Rethink (cited in Manitoba Schizophrenia Society) identify the first of Barber's 'types' but indicate that:

this tends to consider people with mental illness as passive recipients of treatment and services'.

In a position statement consultant psychiatrists (2010) put forward the idea that:

there is no set model of Recovery and it is better to speak about Recovery ideas or concepts'. (p4)

When considering the concept of self-harm there is a general recognition that self-harming behaviour is something that some individuals might 'need' to do at some point due to circumstances that may be occurring in their lives. The fact that it is not necessarily of help to them in the long term is also accepted. It is still difficult to identify with any degree of certainty within this topic answers to the following:

- Why do individuals begin to self-harm?
- What alternative(s) might have been made/identified as available to/for them by either themselves or someone else?
- What motivates the individuals to consider cessation of self-harm?
- Who decides what recovery in the context of self-harm is and when it is occurring or has occurred?

The final point identified above can introduce potential conflict as individuals and services may not necessarily concur with each other regarding outcomes related to self-harm and its reduction and/or cessation. There is still a degree of ambivalence in some services to agreeing that someone who is seeking help and support may continue to periodically self-harm during this process.

There is occasionally a requirement placed on the individual that support will be forthcoming only after they have agreed not to engage in self-harm. In some mental health environments individuals will have any items in their possession that may be potentially used for self-harm removed as part of a risk reduction requirement.

Although as mentioned earlier recovery is limited in terms of literary exploration in the context of self-harm some does exist. Middleton and Garvie (2008) explore recovery in a section of their book. They suggest that it is important for the individual themselves to take the decision to consider the cessation of self-harm/injury and that pressure from others to stop may be detrimental to the individual in their progress towards this end. Another publication (Grocutt, 2009) cites a study that appears to support: *'the application of the recovery model and attachment theory in informing therapeutic work with women who self-harm'*. (p196)

Unfortunately much of the literature within the professional domain of mental health frequently correlates self-harm and suicide and explores ways of 'stopping' the behaviour and less on understanding why people may be engaging in it. It also may compromise the initial encounter with an individual who has presented after self-harming as part of the recommended procedure includes the offer of a psychosocial assessment (NICE, 2012). It is important to stress that without an appropriate explanation, preferably in advance, it may be difficult for the individual to understand the reasoning behind some of the questions that may be asked by the nurse and/or doctor. Here the ability of the professional to communicate sensitively and effectively may be the difference between a positive and negative experience for the person who has self-harmed.

Although some individuals may be concerned about undergoing a psychosocial assessment if they come into contact with mental health services this is an important recommendation that dates back to the NICE guidelines issued in 2004. It is intended to provide those offering support to identify some of the intentions associated with the self-harm incident and then adapt any support accordingly to enable recovery to become a planned part of that process. Unfortunately it would appear that about this time (i.e. 2004) if you attended somewhere such as an Accident and Emergency (A&E) department and had deliberately self-harmed (to use the terminology of the time) then you might expect to have any 'wounds' (this could be considered to be psychological as well as physical!) attended to. There was an awareness that all too frequently the physical injury was attended to with little attempt made to identify or explore the individual's psychological distress.

Providing the individual with the opportunity to talk and listening to them was all too often a rare occurrence and as mentioned previously (for different reasons) is currently difficult for staff to provide within the current frequently overstretched A&E departments.

Another issue that is still apparent is the limited amount of evidence regarding 'appropriate' interventions that may benefit the individual who has self-harmed. Although there is literature that explores interventions for individuals with a recognized mental health problem (e.g. Borderline Personality Disorder; Depression) who also self-harm, for those without a mental health problem there is less clarity. Rossouw and Fonaghy (2012) suggest that a mentalization-based treatment demonstrates some positive signs when compared to 'treatment as usual' in adolescents with depression who self-harmed. Mentalization has been defined as: *'keeping one's own state, desires and goals in mind as one addresses one's own experiences; and keeping another's state, desires, and goals in mind as one interprets his or her behavior'.* Coate (2006) and Washburn et al (2012) in their articles on non-suicidal self-injury (NSSI) express concern that in their search of the literature there is little evidence that psychotherapeutic interventions have been designed and evaluated for NSSI and none that were specifically for adolescents with NSSI.

The attitude of the practitioner is an integral part of the process of care and support and this has a significant impact on the individual's relationship with the service. Self-harm still has the capacity to shock practitioners and instil a mixture of anxiety and a degree of negativity towards the individual presenting for help. This is clearly recognized by Walsh (2008) who states:

'Becoming actively aware of the risks of negative thoughts, feelings, and behaviors can serve to inoculate professionals against acting counterproductively in the treatment. Clients deserve care that is fresh, positive and technically proficient'. (p228)

Another additional factor that needs to be considered is the fact that much of the emphasis in the literature and indeed practice regarding self-harm has a focus around adolescents and young adults. One book published regarding self-harm broadens this focus and the authors (Adler and Adler, 2011) note that 'self-injury' has evolved sociologically and in recognition of the extensive impact of self-harm state in their introduction:

'In this book we describe how self-injury changed from being the limited and hidden practice of the psychologically disordered to becoming a cult youth phenomenon, then a form of more teenage angst, and then the province of a wide swath of socially

disempowered individuals in broader age, race, gender, and class groups' (p2)

There is still however limited material regarding adults and indeed older adults. Toms and Ritchie (2009) in their exploration of how self-harm is managed in older people identified:

'Opinion differed as to whether older people were treated differently'.

Dennis and Owens (2012) identify within their article that specific factors such as *'widowhood, living alone, social isolation and low levels of social support'* are associated with self-harm in older people.

Another variation within the exploration of recovery may be to look at it from a preventative aspect. This means looking at the evidence currently available around reasons why individuals may resort to self-harming and then consider ways in which these may be addressed within a planned preventative strategy. One place where this can start is within the educational system potentially within both the primary and secondary schools where young people frequently encounter self-harm as a way to deal with what is happening to them in this or other situations (e.g. bullying, home circumstances). Hall and Place (2010) in their research looked at what school might offer and identified:

'Working successfully... feeling a sense of achievement... positive friendship networks...positive diversions including physical recreation are all part of a successful school environment'.

Although this helps to qualify some of the attributes that a school has to offer it is unlikely that each child can be sufficiently supported to achieve this. Not all children possess the confidence and skills to develop effective and positive social interactions with their peers and it also potentially compromises those children who may find physical recreation challenging or problematic enough that they actively seek to avoid it.

The importance of achievement/qualifications is further reinforced in a report by The Prince's Trust (2013) that identified the consequences of poor educational attainment/qualifications and the potential 'knock on' effects of unemployment on a young person's self-esteem and mental health. Adding to Hall and Place's focus on might be offered through the school experience MindFull's report (2013) includes ideas that may assist young people deal with some of the many challenges they encounter at school. Within the document there is a recommendation citing four changes that are considered important if the educational environment is to assist young people within the school experience, namely.

1. Early intervention and prevention (include mental health as a core theme in curriculum)

2. Increased professional support and advice
3. Help young people to support each other
4. Provide online access to services

The individual who self-harms and their perception of how they may be progressing is important to consider. It is essential that whoever is supporting the individual recognises this and accommodates this interpretation by actively listening to the individual. In one of the stories contained within a previous book on the subject of self-harm/injury by the author (Wallace, 2012) an individual writing under the pseudonym of 'Ma' in their recognition of progress stated:

Some people call it 'recovery' some say 'being well'. I don't know what to call it so I'm going to go with 'normal'.

Many authors (e.g. Simpson, 2006; McHale & Felton, 2012) have identified that when seeking help, one of the significant obstacles for individuals who self-harm is the negative attitudes they encounter from professionals. Brown and Kimball (2013) are more specific and feel that it is the approach that the practitioners take that needs to change to allow individuals to feel less misunderstood and to acknowledge that self-harm is important and has a significant role in that person's life at that point in time. Because the attitude of others is important it is seen as an element in helping to get better as encapsulated in this statement from a support organization:

'You can also read about some of the myths that surround self-harm – many of which can be barriers to better services and support…the final section will provide you with some information…it is there out of recognition that just telling you to stop won't work, and we want to keep you safe while you recover in your own time'.

This has recently been followed by the development of online resources (e.g. Alumina) to create a *'safe, pro-recovery site for people to use to communicate with others and express their experiences…'* (www.selfharm.co.uk)

Continuing the theme of online support and services MindFull (2013) in their survey and subsequent report made four recommendations regarding mental health. The fourth identified:

'Provide online access to services (Provide access to safe online support services that understand and address the needs of children and young people)' (p. 9).

Other initiatives that have arisen include Internet sites that provide a range of information including stories related to self-harm and recovery. One such site is a collaborative venture between two Canadian universities, namely the University of Guelph and McGill

University. SIOS (Self-Injury Outreach and Support) includes brief quotes from individuals such as the one cited here:
'Like everyone says, self-injury urges are part of recovery. I haven't cut in 10 months. I still get urges from time to time but the time between them gets longer. It gets better if that makes sense. Keep fighting everyone, you're doing well'. (SIOS)

Services attempting to improve the way in which they engage and support individuals who self-harm may look at an alternative approach that may have a more positive outcome such as that suggested by Allen (2007). This requires mental health services to focus on any underlying distress rather than the actual self-harm that may be visible. Within a mental health context, Ougrin et al (2013) identified within their study a positive outcome when mental health staff were provided with specific training related to self-harm. The impact of this training, which was based on therapeutic assessment, was viewed on a before and after basis regarding issues such as understanding and attitudes. This theme of staff training is important and is explored again by James et al (2012) in a literature review but here it looks at staff attitudes and notes that further research is needed to:

'develop a model of meaningful nursing care for people who self-harm during an admission. This could help to reduce feelings of helplessness and frustration among nursing staff, and increase their knowledge and skills, as well as feelings of hope for recovery' (p307).

Long et al (2012) in exploring a more holistic view in relation to the subject indicate that self-harm may be more positively addressed by staff through the concept of *'a shared piece of human experience'.*

A small study by Sinclair and Green (2005) introduced an interesting perspective regarding the views of some individuals who self-harmed. It indicates that one of the issues that existed and viewed as positive was that of admission to hospital as an element of recovery for some of the individuals interviewed. Although some may perceive this option as a retrograde step, for a number of individuals the process of admission to a specialist mental health unit was regarded by them as an important part of the intervention, support and subsequent recovery process.

One area that continues to court controversy is that of the use of harm minimization as a strategy to support individuals who are receiving professional care. Advocates suggest that this approach enables individuals to retain a degree of control that is important to them. They also state that it helps to avoid the risk of people who self-harm moving from a managed process to one that may escalate risk. This could occur through individuals who have been denied access to their 'normal' process being forced to look for alternative means/items they can acquire when feeling desperate thus reducing control about what is used, when, where and how. Pembroke (2009) in the DVD 'Cutting the Risk' states:

'Harm minimization is about accepting the need to self-harm as a valid method of survival until survival is possible by other means. It doesn't encourage or condone self-injury. It is about maximizing safety in the event of it'.

Shaw and Shaw (2007) identify in their chapter that attempts are frequently made when people encounter mental health services to prevent opportunities for self-harming to take place by removing any potential items deemed dangerous. This is considered as counterproductive in supporting the individuals as:

'In practice, it appears to be impossible to prevent someone from self-injuring regardless of what restrictions are put in place. Furthermore, as the self-injury takes place in a very 'out of control' manner because of the methods used and because of the secrecy and urgency, it follows then that the injuries that result are potentially more damaging'. (p30)

Freeman (2010) in her book offers yet another alternative interpretation that incorporates practitioners, self-harming and the individual:

'However, what all nurses, doctors, clinicians and therapists need to realize is that by focusing on the harm-the action-you are becoming a character in the drama of the person's self-harm: you are becoming the rescuer. They must realize-and you, the parent, must also realize- that there is no such person who can keep the young person safe. With support and great patience, they must take responsibility themselves: they must keep themselves safe'. (p118)

NICE (2011) indicates there is a need for further research around this area and concludes Section 4.5 stating:

'Although cessation of the behaviour remains the treatment goal for many professionals providing care to people who self-harm, this may not be realistic or possible in the short term for some individuals. An alternative strategy for services is to reduce the severity and frequency of self-harm'. (p31)

In an article reflecting some of the material contained within the NICE (2011) guidelines Shaw (2012) identified concerns that were still evident with professionals and their employing organisations feeling anxious:

'around suicide and severe injury, alongside fears of transgressing codes of conduct and 'duty of care', and subsequent criminal or civil proceedings'.

However she also stated towards the end of the article:

'Rather, with adequate support and supervision, those concerns can help to inform a thoughtful, individualised response to self-harm, one which fits more closely with the core principles of a helpful response as identified by people who self-harm, and the people who care for them'.

The S.A.F.E. ALTERNATIVES programme offered in the US differs markedly in this respect by asking those who want to participate in the programme to not self-harm:

'Upon admission a safety contract is signed, in which the patient agrees to refrain from any self-injurious behaviors for the entire length of the treatment'. (30-Day Programme)

Middleton and Garvie (2008) identify in their book that: 'the first step is to decide that you do want to stop' (p57). The question of whether this is a decision arrived at by the individual without any influence from others or through interventions by others is still a contentious issues as identified in some of the material cited previously.

Strong identifies a change in one individual offered as an example within her book thus: 'she no longer wanted to hurt herself' (p160). By way of contrast Conterio and Lader (1998) state:

'We can never tell which of our patients are going to recover and which ones seem unable-or unwilling-to get better...recovery from self-injury seems not to correlate directly to the severity or frequency of the symptoms' (p286)

In attempting to pull together the key elements of their book exploring the topic from a strong psychotherapeutic perspective, Tantam and Huband (2009) identify:

'giving up self-injury requires considerable determination, but just trying hard is not enough'. (p200)

The above view is shared to some extent in work by Wills (2012) who suggests that recovery in the context of self-harm may be viewed in two different ways, namely:

'as an incremental process or ongoing journey and also as a definitive outcome which was largely perceived as unattainable and inconceivable by the participants'.

Furnivall (2013) identifies a number of strategies that may be of assistance for young people self-harming such as:

'Many young people also find it useful to use diaries and visual ways to begin to recognize patterns in their own behaviour and then to begin to exert some control over it' (p18)

In looking at the common threads that enable self-harm and recovery to be explored together we may include both the role (or preparation for role) of others and self as indicated in these examples:

'Recovery is an important, new idea which has radical implications for the design and operation of mental health services. There are clearly obstacles to its implementation. To help to overcome them, there might be a value in thinking about a recovery-orientated 'Policy Implementation Guide' to provide simple guidelines for practice at an individual, team and service level.' (Shepherd et al, 2008)

Pietruszan (2010) identified four factors that can help contribute to the recovery process, namely: -

- Motivation
- Openness and honesty with oneself
- An involved support system
- Commitment to treatment and self-care (Pietruszan, 2010)

Summary:

It can be seen from the diversity of opinion that exists when looking at self-harming behaviour and recovery that this is a complex task. It has to encapsulate the views of a wide range of individuals, circumstances and groups. As a result of this it is not unusual to find a diverse range of proposed strategies suggested for professionals when engaging with and offering support and interventions for self-harming behaviour. The different terminologies, research methodologies and incidence rates that exist in the available international literature do not aid attempts to arrive at some degree of consistency, something clearly identified in the article on international prevalence by Muehlenkamp et al (2012).

Both self-harm and recovery continue to be terms that attract a wide range of interpretation and therefore it is not surprising that misunderstandings arise. Interventions are currently one of the areas that continue to attract widely differing opinions. Issues around the most effective use of harm-minimisation and/or reduction are widely dispersed and until there is some conciliation on these services and those who access them there will continue to be disagreement on what constitutes 'best practice'.

Considering this fact (i.e. that many people involved do not always agree on what constitutes the 'best' approach) the following points may help to illustrate some of the current considerations that contribute to this:

- The view that self-harm is a dysfunctional activity and therefore should be discontinued (either before or during support/intervention)

- The view that self-harm is a survival strategy for some individuals and may be incorporated within any recovery plan
- The view that harm-minimisation is an effective strategy but the interpretation of what it means is viewed very differently by the various groups/individuals involved
- The view that recovery is something that applies to 'mainstream' mental health services and therefore has little or no relevance to self-harming behaviour that occurs independently of any identified mental health problems
- The view that recovery itself is a misguided term and needs to be revisited and reviewed to aid clarity

Irrespective of the difficulties that arise from attempting to untangle the variety of views, opinions and interpretations of both self-harm and recovery it is important to accommodate the diversity of opinion as a representation of current thinking. This is an essential element if we are to arrive at a point where all the participants are able to listen to and learn from one another to potentially acquire a shared understanding.

Subsequent chapters will investigate the relationship from a variety of perspectives and therefore allow the reader to explore both the variation and value that emerge regarding the importance of considering 'discovery' (as some individuals are now introducing as the alternative term for recovery!).

It is important to incorporate the idea that for many people who self-harm there comes a point where a change in that person's status is then reflected in a reduction in the need for or dependence on self-harm. How this is considered, viewed and indeed achieved should be acknowledged. This is irrespective of the agreement or otherwise on the terminology that may be utilized in an attempt to explain or understand the change that has occurred.

References:

Adler P.A., and Adler P. (2011) The Tender Cut: Inside the Hidden World of Self-Injury, London, New York University Press

Anthony W.A. (1993), Recovery from Mental Illness: The Guiding Vision of the Mental Health Service System in the 1990s, Psychosocial Rehabilitation Journal, 16(4), pp.11-23

Barber M.E. (2012), Recovery as the New Medical Model for Psychiatry, Psychiatric Services, Vol. 63, No. 3, available online at http://ps.psychiatryonline.org/article.aspx?articleid=1028618 (accessed 6th January 2014)

Brown T.B., and Kimball T. (2013), Cutting to Live: A Phenomenology of Self harm, Journal of Marital and Family Therapy, Vol. 39, No. 2, pp.195-208

Coates S.W. in Allen J.G., and Fonaghy P. (Eds), (2006), Handbook of Mentalization-Based Treatment, Chicester, John Wiley and Sons Ltd.

Conterio K., and Lader W. (1998), Bodily harm: The Breakthrough Healing Program for Self-Injurers, New York, Hyperion

Davidson L. (2005), Recovery, self-management and the expert patient – Changing the culture of mental health from a UK perspective, Journal of Mental Health, 14(1), pp.25-35

Dennis M.S., and Owens D.W. (2012) Self-harm in older people: a clear need for specialist assessment and care, The British Journal of Psychiatry, 200, pp.356-358

Freeman J. (2010), cover up: Understanding Self-Harm, Dublin, Veritas

Furnivall J. (2013), Understanding suicide and self-harm amongst children in care and care leavers, Glasgow, IRISS

Grocutt E., in Motz A. (Ed), (2009), Managing Self-Harm: Psychological Perspectives, Hove, Routledge

Hall B., and Place M. (2010), Cutting to Cope – a modern adolescent phenomenon, Child: care, health and development, 36, 5, pp.623-629

James K., Stewart D., and Bowers L. (2012), Self-harm and attempted suicide within inpatient psychiatric services: A review of the literature, International Journal of Mental Health Nursing, 21, pp.301-309

Kemp R. (2009), Self-harm Practice Reference Guide, NCERC

Long M., Manktelow R., and Tracey A. (2012), We are all in this together: working towards a holistic understanding of self-harm, Journal of Psychiatric and Mental Health Nursing, pp.1-9

Middleton K., and Garvie S. (2008), Self-Harm: The Path to Recovery, Oxford, Lion Hudson plc.

MindFull. (2013), "Alone with my thoughts". Recommendations for a new approach to young people's mental health support

Mountain D., and Shah P.J. (2008), Recovery and the medical model (editorial), Advances in Psychiatric Treatment, Vol. 14, pp.241-244

Muehlenkamp J.J., Claes L., Havertape L., and Plener P.L. (2012), International prevalence of adolescent non-suicidal self-injury and deliberate self-harm, Child and Adolescent Psychiatry and mental Health, 6:10, Open Access at http://www.capmh.com/content/pdf/1753-2000-8-13.pdf (accessed 4th July 2014)

NICE. (2011), Self-harm: longer-term management, NICE clinical guideline 133, Manchester, National Institute for Health and Clinical Excellence

NICE. (2012), Review of Clinical Guideline (CG16) - Self-harm: The short-term physical and psychological management and secondary prevention of self-harm in primary and secondary care, available at: http://www.nice.org.uk/nicemedia/live/10946/58110/58110.pdf (accessed 20th May 2014)

NSW CAG. (2009), Literature Review on Recovery, Sydney, New South Wales Consumer Advisory Group

Ougrin D., Zundel T., Ng A.V., Habel B., and Latif S. (2013), Teaching Therapeutic Assessment for self-harm in adolescents: Training Outcomes, Psychology and Psychotherapy: Theory, Research and Practice, 86, pp.70-85

Pembroke L. (2009), Cutting the Risk: self-harm minimization in perspective, NSHMG

Pietruszan C. (2010), Recovering from self-injury (Fact sheet) Cornell Research Program in Self-Injurious Behavior in Adolescents and Young Adults. Retrieved from http://www.selfinjury.bctr.cornell.edu/factsheet_recovery.asp

Rethink, Recovery From Severe Mental Illness, cited in Manitoba Schizophrenia Society, available online at http://www.mss.mb.ca/resource_materials_details.php?id=14 (accessed 7th January 2014)

Rossouw T.I., and Fonaghy P. (2012), Mentalization-Based Treatment for Self-Harm in Adolescents: A Randomized Control Trial, Journal of the American Academy of Child and Adolescent Psychiatry, Vol. 51, Issue 12, pp.1304-1313

www.selfharm.co.uk, Get information, The Facts; The myths; Staying safe (accessed 13th January 2014)

S.A.F.E. http://www.selfinjury.com/referrals/programs/ (accessed 29th April, 2014)

Shaw C. (2012), Harm-minimisation for self-harm, mentalhealth, September/October, pp.19-21

Shaw C., and Shaw T., in Spandler H., and Warner S. (Eds), (2007), Beyond Fear and Control: working with young people who self-harm, Ross-on-Wye, PCCS Books Ltd.

Shepherd G., Boardman J., and Slade M. (2008), Making Recovery a Reality, Sainsbury Centre for Mental Health, London

Sinclair J., and Green J. (2005), Understanding resolution of deliberate self-harm: qualitative interview study of patients' experiences, BMJ, doi: 10.1136/bmj.38441.503333.8F (published 20 April 2005)

SIOS, Your stories, your quotes, http://www.sioutreach.org/help-and-recovery/you-are-not-alone, (accessed 16th July 2014)

South London and Maudsley NHS Foundation Trust and South West London and St George's Mental Health NHS Trust. (2010), Recovery is for ALL. Hope, Agency and Opportunity in Psychiatry. A Position Statement by Consultant Psychiatrists. London. SLAM/SWLSTG

Strong M. (1998), A Bright Red Scream: self-mutilation and the language of pain, Middlesex, Penguin

Tantam D., and Huband N. (2009), Understanding Repeated Self-Injury: A Multidisciplinary Approach, Basingstoke, Palgrave Macmillan

The Prince's Trust. (2013), Youth Index 2014

Wallace B. (2012), Self-Harm/Injury: An Exploration of Attitudes and Issues From Literature and Personal Stories, Brentwood, Chipmunkapublishing

Walsh B.W. (2008), Treating Self-Injury: A Practical Guide, London, The Guildford Press

Washburn J.J., Richardt S.L., Styler D.M., Gebhardt M., Juzwin K.R., Yourek A., and Aldridge D. (2012), Psychotherapeutic approaches to non-suicidal self-injury in adolescents, Child and Adolescent Psychiatry and Mental Health, 6:14, Open Access available at http://www.capmh.com/content/6/1/14 (accessed 4th July 2014)

Wills K.A. (2012), What Does Recovery Mean to Adults who Self-Injure? An Interpretative Phenomenological Analysis, International Journal of Psychosocial Rehabilitation, Vol. 17(1), pp.93-116, available at

http://www.psychosocial.com/IJPR_17/What_Does_Recovery_Mean_Wills.html, (accessed 13th July 2014)

'Brian'

I would say that I'm "in recovery", as it's only been a few months since my last self-harm. Perhaps once it gets to more than 6 months I would class myself as recovered.
I'll give you a brief background on my experiences with self-harm.

My self-harming started back in 1997 when I was at university. I was struggling a bit with stress due to exam worries and course work pressure. I had found self-harming was helping to reduce my stress.

I had occasional self-harm issues off and on over the next two years, eventually graduating in 1999. I was still having issues with self-harm over the next few years, gradually stopping from around 2003 onwards. During this time I had seen a psychologist regarding my depression and self-harm. I had been put on antidepressant medication, which although it eased the depression, didn't help with the self-harm.

My self-harm escalated from 2009 onwards, when I was going through a difficult period. As well as suffering from depression, I was having issues with my manager at work. This escalated and I was signed off with work related stress from late 2010, eventually leaving my job in March 2011 by a compromise agreement. During this period I was very stressed, and self-harming regularly. I was also seeing a clinical psychiatrist regularly with regards to my self-harm.

After being discharged from the psychiatrist early 2010, I was pretty much left to get on with things myself, although I was still seeing my GP regularly for antidepressant medication. I felt that the psychiatrists and GP were just looking at me as someone who is depressed and someone who is self- harming, and they tried to fix those problems without looking at me as a whole person, and look at why I felt how I did.

During the summer of 2011, I was seeing a support worker at an Employment Access Trust, which is a group which helps people with mental health issues get back into work. I found them very helpful, they gave me a lot of support to get my CV up to date and boost my self-confidence, which was quite low after leaving my last job. I was introduced to Penumbra by my support worker at the Employment Access Trust.

Bruce Wallace

I started Penumbra in August 2011. I found I got a lot of help with regards to understanding my self-harm, and my triggers for doing so. The support workers ('O', then 'M') were very helpful and looked at me as a whole person. I found by them doing this, I was able to better understand my reasons for self-harming, and look at ways to reduce and recover from self- harming behaviour.

I also started college at this time, studying conservation. (National Certificate in Conservation and Countryside Recreation). I was open with my college tutors regarding my mental health issues, and I also saw staff at the student support department who were able to give me help with regards to managing my studies and workload.

I found that college was really good for me; it helped boost my self-confidence as well as social skills. Combined with the support from Penumbra I managed to successfully complete the course.

With regards to the Penumbra self-harm project, I found it was very useful. Rather than focussing solely on stopping me self-harming, the support workers encouraged me to look at why I self-harm, and ways to reduce it. They looked at me as a whole person. One thing which 'M' encouraged me to do was to come up with "rules for life", which I could use to remind myself to stay well. I have included a copy of these in appendix A.

I would say that after all the support from my support worker at Penumbra that I am in recovery from self-harm. Although I still get occasional urges, I now understand that self-harming will not really solve anything long-term.

Chapter 2
SELF-HARM AND RECOVERY: A COLLECTIVE, BUT NOT CONSENSUS VIEW
- **Naomi Salisbury (with additional input from Tina Luke; Nicci; Lainey Templeton; Amanda O'Connell; EJ Strunk and Gwen McLeod and others who chose not to be specifically named)**

- Introduction

"It seems like a lot of people wonder when exactly you're recovered. 6 months clean? A year? More? Less? I really think it's up to the individual. When you can say with complete confidence that you are never, ever going back there, and you're taking every possible measure to ensure that you don't, then that's recovery. I was clean for almost a year, and a lot of people might consider themselves to be recovered after that time, but I knew in my heart I wasn't finished. I wasn't ready to give it up. It's certainly a difficult journey, but it's attainable, if you truly want it and put every effort into it. Never give up. Something will work for you. If you haven't found it yet, keep searching. Something will help. It won't be easy, but it's worth the fight."

- About this piece of work

This chapter is the result of a small piece of consultation work by CAPS Advocacy based in the Lothian region of Scotland. Much of our work focuses on collecting and acting on the views of people with personal experience of mental health issues and treatment. We aim to be pro-active in supporting people to raise issues with services and campaign for changes and improvements in services rather than solely responding to consultation requests from services. In our collective advocacy service we look to represent the range of views on any given topic, rather than one person speaking for a heterogeneous group.

We also work closely with a range of people who use self-harm, partly due to specific advocacy projects and partly due to strong links with other services and community groups. When we heard about this book proposal we felt it was a good opportunity to gather a wide variety of views to be presented in a collective first person format to contrast with personal views and experiences and anonymised research.

To collate the information in this chapter we simply asked: *What would you like to say about self-harm and recovery?*

- A note from the author

In writing this chapter I wanted to express very passionately the variety of views people have on self-harm and recovery and in particular their relation to one another. I could write screeds on this topic, as I feel very strongly that there is no specific way to define recovery in relation to self -harm. To try undermines both the concept of recovery, as I understand it, and all of my learning about the individual nature of the use of self -harm. I feel equally passionately about representing a range of views, not just the ones which are loudest, and the result is this chapter which I hope is informative and challenging in equal measures. I have used people's own words as much as possible as I feel nothing can capture their experience better than this. It has been an illuminating and humbling piece of work for me and I can only hope that readers will appreciate people giving freely of their very personal experiences in order to educate others.

- Definitions of Recovery?

The Scottish Recovery Network defines recovery as:
"Recovery is being able to live a meaningful and satisfying life, as defined by each person, in the presence or absence of symptoms. It is about having control over and input into your own life. Each individual's recovery, like his or her experience of the mental health problems or illness, is a unique and deeply personal process."
However they also acknowledge that:
"In talking about recovery we acknowledge that it is not necessarily easy or straightforward. Many people describe the need to persevere and to find ways to maintain hope through the most trying times."
While running the consultation on self-harm and recovery CAPS tried as hard as possible to make it clear that the organisation has no specific view on recovery and that all and any views were welcome in the consultation.
In CAPS experience there are a variety of views of recovery that range from very positive to people who feel it is not useful or reflective of their experiences in any way. As an advocacy organisation we feel it is very important to represent all of these views, especially when recovery has become a very dominant discourse in mental health services. However, it is important to

remember that the current concept of recovery came from mental health activists and explicitly states that it is a unique personal experience, which may or may not involve on-going support.

The initial aim of using the word recovery was to turn the tide away from deficit-focused services and concentrate on strengths and assets at least on an equal footing with needs and issues. Some people feel that the recovery concept has been 'hijacked' by mainstream statutory services and fundamentally changed from the originally intended meaning.

As statutory services have embraced the concept of recovery it has become less a self-defined experience so much as part of a pre-defined healthcare pathway. In Scotland there is a strong focus on recovery, but a lack of consensus on the meaning and how this might look in terms of support and treatment. It is becoming increasingly difficult to be someone who does not 'sign up' to the concept of recovery. On the other hand huge changes in approach and services have been brought about with the more positive and hopeful focus that recovery has injected into mental health services.

Results of the Survey

112 people responded to an anonymous online survey over one month. As the title indicates the results gave us a collective, not a consensus view. The responses showed both consensus and a wide variety of opinions. Both broad and narrow views of what recovery could mean were expressed and this also impacted on whether people felt recovery was possible.

- What is Recovery?

"Self-harm is easy, but recovery is hard."

Throughout the survey responses there was a strong indication or implication that 'recovery from self-harm' meant 'stopping'; however, this was a concept that seemed to be associated with others' expectations rather than the personal beliefs of people responding to the survey.

"There's no easy way to sugar coat this - recovery is hard. It's hard, painful and a lot of the time a solitary, uphill climb. And the thing most people forget is that recovery isn't so much a destination; where one is magically "cured", but more a daily journey of choosing life, choosing healthy coping mechanisms, choosing to not let the pain take over."

Recovery as defined by the Scottish Recovery Network is seen a unique and individual experience and this was reflected in people's views on the concept of recovery.

Recovery was described in a variety of ways; all of them different; none of them completely tangible.

Recovery:

- ...is something you have to want
- ...isn't linear
- ...is gradual
- ...is different for everyone
- ...is a hard concept to wrap your head around
- ...is very hard

Whether recovery has anything to do with using self-harm was another consideration for many people and followed a continuum from an absolute relationship to tangential one. The one thing there was consensus on however was that recovery in whatever form it takes is difficult on every level.

"*Modest improvements, such as a decrease in frequency or the severity of the harm seem to go overlooked. It is a change in thought and behaviour. Even though I hated relapse into the behaviour, I had to learn to celebrate progress.*"

"*Recovery for me is a lifelong task of becoming more self-aware and self-accepting, learning to love myself as fully as I am able. It is not something that can be done to me or applied by another through treatment regardless of their medical or professional expertise. That said I can be, and often have been, assisted in the ongoing process of recovery and the involvement of another human being in that can be critical in learning to trust others and experience the world as a safe place*"

"*Although I would say I am recovered from self-harming, I am still on a journey of healing, so to speak. That is, learning to value myself and to know what it feels like to have confidence and self-belief. Recognising all my emotions and feelings and being able to experience them.*"

"*I haven't self-harmed in a long time, which might be seen by some as "recovery" from self-harm. I don't think of it like that and if a professional talked in terms to me when I was in crisis, I would find that incredibly difficult and triggering. Self-harm continues to be an option and knowing I have it has helped me a lot in a recent period of distress, though I did not use it.*"

"*Unless you truly want to quit, and have support you won't. Same as smoking, same as anything. You have to want it 100%. I think self-harm and many other similar conditions need to be treated like addictions.*"

"Once you start, it's one of the hardest things you will ever have to do to stop. It takes over your life, your thoughts, and it overcomes you. It becomes who you are. It's terrifying when someone tries to take it away from you. It is not a death wish, it's a life wish."

As well as the broader concepts of what recovery might mean there were also a variety of views on what recovery means on a more practical level. Although there was a concept of recovery being seen as no longer using self-harm, the personal views of what recovery looks like covered a range of experiences. In addition many people asked the question whether their version of recovery 'counted', especially if it involved thoughts or use of self-harm.

Recovery:
- …is when you have to want to stop altogether
- …is stopping but still have urges
- …is being able to resist the urge
- …is doing it less than I used to
- …is when it's no longer a first resort
- …is when I need it less

"I would say that for now and for the last 2 and half years of my life I am a recovered self-harmer. Not in recovery; but recovered!"

"Recovery for me will be not using the self-injury behaviours to cope and to a lesser extent, other things which will harm me in the long run."

- **"For me recovery is about being able to resist the urges,"**

"Even after three years free from self-harm, a person can have a relapse, so even being self-harm free for years cannot help a person relax and feel assured that they are okay. The worry of a relapse is always there".

"Even if you're "in recovery" the thought is always there in the back of your mind."

"To me, recovery means being able to resist the impulse to self-harm. I haven't harmed myself in seven years, yet the urges have never gone away. At times, I still come dangerously close to relapsing. It's something I believe I'll struggle with for the rest of my life."

"That I don't engage in the behaviour. The emotions don't stop. The justifications wouldn't end if I was seeking a reason to justify self-harm."

"I don't think living in recovery from self-harm is about never doing it again, I believe it is far more about the learning of alternative

41

coping strategies and the understanding that occasionally self-harm might be the only thing left to do when those strategies fail."

These responses also threw up a very thought provoking question - does not using self-harm mean recovery if you still feel the same?

"I sometimes wonder if not harming anymore is a true sign of recovery. Is recovery more than giving self-harm up, especially if you still want to harm, but choose not to?"

So, Is Recovery Possible?

"Recovery from self-harm is possible but not easy at all. It is similar to treating an addict, relapses are very common and the urges can be irresistible. Recovery wouldn't be stopping the injury but more of learning how to cope with emotions and directing that negative energy somewhere other than on oneself."

As well as definitions of recovery a major theme was whether recovery was possible, regardless of whether it could be defined or not.

A small number of people felt recovery that equated with no longer using self-harm was possible.

"Things have changed and I don't need it anymore."

"In self-harm recovery for me has been about stopping the behaviour."

"I have now thrown away my "just in case razor" and just hope I can continue on the way to a life without self-harm."

But for a much larger group of others things were not so concrete.

"Recovery from self-harm - I chuckle at that term because even now with more than three years without self-harming I still have urges. I think that self-harm is in many ways similar to using drugs or alcohol. You learn what your triggers are; you learn healthy ways of dealing with life stresses - even the big ones. Yet there are always times when your mind will flash onto the 'easy way' of dealing with the pain. Recovery isn't easy, there are times of relapse. The thing that is most important is a commitment to yourself to stop using self-harm as a way of dealing with things."

"I don't feel that recovery is ever completed. In my personal experience the underlying drive to self-harm isn't gone, but I am no longer acting on the impulse. I consider myself recovered on that basis."

"I don't think you can ever recover, you just move to a place where you don't want to do it anymore, but the underlying urge never goes away, I can never say I am recovered, but I have learned not to use that as a strategy anymore."

Fuzzy at the Edges

"Is there any real recovery or is it just periods of time where you just happen to win the struggle?"

Other people gave even broader concepts of what recovery might or might not be, questioning both the ideas and the practical activities involved:

"The only type of recovery I know of is to just try and struggle. Same as quitting smoking I guess, you try to quit and you do for a while, then you fall off the wagon. This, I'm thinking will have to happen several times before any real progress is made. I sometimes consider myself a recovering Self-Injurer, but am I really? Most days cutting is all I can think of and all I want. Am I really trying to recover or am I just making my life that much harder?"

"Recovering from self-harm is not a linear process. You don't go from self-harming to not self-harming along one straight path. Like with many things in life, it is a case of taking steps forward and steps back in the general direction of not hurting yourself. The idea that you just suddenly stop having the urge to hurt yourself isn't true. Learning to deal with those urges in a way that doesn't harm you is a long and difficult journey."

- Recovery isn't Possible

"Self-harm, for me, means several things. It's the one thing that I can turn to at any point of the day, 24-7. It has become my best friend, my confidant, the one consistency in my life. People ask, 'why self-harm though?', and the answer is 'for several reasons'. Sometimes, it's purely to feel something, something physical, to release that mind fog that consumes you when depression and self-loathing takes over. Other times it's as a punishment; you get a bad grade, you cut, you eat too many calories, you cut; but eventually that punishment becomes an addiction to just feel something other. You get complimented, you cut. Something good happens, or something bad and you cut, you burn and you do anything to get out of the skin you live in. Similarly, sometimes, it purely is just to see the pain you feel inside inflicted somewhere on your outer self; your mind laid in front of your eyes, maybe."

A significant number of respondents stated they didn't think recovery was possible for a variety of reasons. For some people the reasons for recovery not being possible were the same as others' definitions of recovery, particularly still having thoughts of self-harm and urges to self-harm. For some people no longer using

43

self-harm was not something they aimed to do, and therefore felt that recovery as it is seen in the wider context was not relevant to them. i.e.:

- …because I still self-injure, although less than I used to
- …because I have stopped but still have urges
- …because I need it and can't stop
- …because It's something that will be there, when everything and everyone else isn't
- …because I never stop thinking about it
- …because I can't conceive of it
- …because I like how it feels
- …because it's always an option
- …because it's not something 'wrong' in the first place
- …because it gives me control

"*It is an addiction. There is something very dark, seductive about it; it's very personal and very powerful.*"

"*I have nothing to say about recovery as I am nowhere near recovered. As for self-harm, it varies to suit my tolerance to the immense emotional pain I am feeling on said day.*"

"*I just can't see a day when I don't resort to these behaviours in some way.*"

"*I don't know if I will ever be able to get rid of the thoughts, and at the moment, I don't know if I want to.*"

- Functions of Self-Harm

"*I find it the fastest and most effective way to keep my emotions in check.*"

People identified a range of reasons why self-harm was not necessarily something they need or want to recover from – it serves a purpose and is not something that needs to be recovered from.

- Addiction
- Punishment
- Escape
- Numbness
- Release
- Anchor
- Changes emotional and physical state
- Safety
- About Survival NOT Suicide

Self-harm as a survival tool and a suicide prevention tool was also identified as an important function of self-harm.

"*Self-harm is not always a precursor to suicide. I am consistently frustrated by people whom link Self-harm to suicidal behaviours. For me, Self-harm is a lifeline and coping mechanism that takes me out of a place where suicide is a danger. I have never made plans to kill myself in my ten years of self-harming.*"

"*I will never be ashamed that I self-harmed because it kept me holding on at a time in my life when I wanted to let go.*"

"*I strongly believe that self-harm for myself was my way of preventing me thinking about stuff I wasn't ready to think about. It also helped me cope with deep feelings of despair and prevented me from thinking more suicidal thoughts.*"

"*The logic of suffering emotionally to avoid more scars is beyond me but to function in our society I have to subscribe to this view.*"

"*Self-harm, even just the thought of it, the comfort of knowing that I can do it if I need to, is what's keeping me alive at the moment.*"

"*Self-harm served many purposes, it was a release, an escape— essentially it served as an emotional anchor which I could rely on to suddenly change my emotional and physical state even in the most difficult situations.*"

Not the Right Term?

Many people expressed the view that 'recovery' was not the most appropriate or accurate term for their experiences, aims and hopes. There was also a feeling that self-harm was seen as an illness in relation to the term recovery when for many it is a constructive tool that has helped them.

Other suggestions were:

- In recovery
- Recovering
- Overcoming
- Journey to self-discovery
- Journey to self-understanding
- Growth

"*I don't know when the term 'recovered' is actually relevant. I know that even after years of being free from it, people still find it difficult to cope with urges, and some often relapse. I don't think there is a specific amount of time that can be applied as to when an individual has 'recovered' from self-harm, rather it is when they are completely free from all urges of it, and maybe don't even think* about it. Maybe 'in recovery' is a more suitable term to describe the process when an individual refrains from self-harm, either for a week or for years."

"Recovery is the wrong word. I don't feel like it's an illness or something wrong with you in the first place. For me it's been a way to cope with extreme distress and feelings of hopelessness. Maybe overcoming is a better word, implying a degree of control over it rather than it controlling you."

"I prefer using the phrase 'journey to self-discovery (or self-understanding)'...for me this means that I am not trying to get rid of my experiences but get to know them, understand them, listen to their purpose and meaning and most importantly thank them for playing a part in my survival."

"I see "recovery" as something not related to self-harm alone. I think it is more about the whole person... Self-harm is a symptom, not a cause, and I think it's not possible to "recover" from self-harm without "recovering" from the problems that are causing the self-harm. Otherwise the recovery is cosmetic rather than actual. I find the word "recovery" a little inappropriate."

"I think that change will be as a result of growth, not of recovery. "Recovery", I think, suggests that I would become something that people in general believe to be good, whereas "growth" suggests that I develop as a person, becoming stronger and more mature while staying the same person I have always been."

"Whilst I rarely cut or burn myself as I once did, I'd be hesitant to say I'd recovered. I've learnt better methods to cope with stress, and having had a few more years to learn how to deal with life I feel I can make a more considered choice with how to cope. I think for me I can never say I'm completely 'recovered' as self-harm will always be there as an option, a fall-back if you will, for if I reach the end of my tether. That's as good as I feel I can hope for on a personal level."

- Set Up to Fail?

It was also pointed out that an expectation or hope of 'recovery' as meaning no longer using self-harm can be counterproductive.

"I don't care much for the term 'recovery' when talking about self-harm. Some people may go weeks or months or even years without self harming and then they become overwhelmed with the urge to do it. And when they do so, the feeling of failure because now they aren't 'recovered' anymore can lead them down a bad path".

- How did I get to a Place Where I Felt Recovery was Possible?

"As I began to love myself, I sought out more constructive ways to release these intense feelings—ways that were creative and enterprising not harmful to myself and others. I had to make the change; I had to make the choice."

A number of themes emerged from the survey about what people had found helpful. However it is important to note that many of the respondents did not consider themselves to be in 'recovery' whether or not they still used self-harm.

- Making Sense of Things

"Until I learned how to understand and express my own emotions I was not able to stop self-harming. Though learning about myself and accepting that I was my own problem I was able to learn not to self-harm and to express myself without fear. To me self-harm is a little like stuttering; it is an illness of the fear of self-expression and the fear of people "getting underneath the surface"

"I have had some counselling, although not specifically to deal with the self-harming. It helped me to realise that things that had happened in the past, and the fact that I really had no one to talk to or trust, did make me more susceptible to self-harming."

"I personally feel that the nature of the condition and recovery is the same for everyone. You need to treat the source of the self-harm first. The cutting is a result not the problem. Without understand why a person turns to cutting recovery will be impossible."

"It isn't something that can just be talked about and overcome quickly. I struggled with it for 6 years before being able to stop. If I sought to self -harm I would find a way to no matter what my surroundings were. I needed to process the reasons for self-harm in order to figure out where I could make changes in coping. I needed a safe place to examine the emotional wounds. I needed to understand why. I needed to hear that I wasn't crazy for how I felt even if I wasn't coping with it appropriately. Listening and being supportive were the most helpful things that could be done to help me recover."

- Feeling Supported in the Right Way

"For me, the key to recovery is feeling supported and valued in your decision to continue or stop self-harming and knowing that you are

the one who will make this decision and that you are not alone in the struggle."

"Recovery is possible with the right support. Support that doesn't focus on the actual cutting, rather the feelings; emotions."

"Recovery comes about when support doesn't focus on injuries."

"It also took professional help from someone who taught me new ways of dealing with things while helping me to learn what my triggers are. Some days it took his belief that I could do it because my own belief in self wasn't as strong. Do I think people who self-harm can stop on their own without help? Of course I do. I also believe that having the help of people who will listen and that you can trust to offer the support during those difficult times makes it much easier."

Acceptance

"When I stopped waiting for a point in my life when I could say "I have recovered" or "I no longer self-harm" at which point I could begin my 'real' journey and began to realise that where I was, was already the journey...things began to shift for me."

"Other people who self-harm were more influential in my achieving recovery than professional because they didn't try to force change when I wasn't ready for it."

- Finding Alternatives

"Recovery is about relying on more adaptive coping methods."

"Having stopped for so long is a source of strength and the willpower to fight is still there."

"I think helping someone who self-harms can be fairly simple. You hopefully would be there to listen, maybe even be available at random times of the day/night to help them cope with a strong urge. Suggesting that someone get exercise or go do something healthy can backfire sometimes, as it sounds like lecturing rather than really caring. A more appropriate way might be to explain how you personally deal with stress or upsetting emotions. Removing the tools a person has used to self -harm is not something that will help them, even if it sounds sensible to an outsider."

Summary

- There appears to be a widely held public and healthcare perception that recovery from self-harm is to no longer use self-harm
- However, there is no uniform view of recovery amongst people who use self-harm
- Some people who use self-harm don't feel that the word 'recovery' is an accurate term to describe their experiences
- As well as no longer using self-harm, control and acceptance were considered signs of recovery
- No longer using self-harm doesn't equal recovery
- No longer using self-harm does not necessarily indicate a reduction in emotional distress or urges to self-harm
- Self-harm is not necessarily something you need to recover from
- Self-harm can be a powerful tool for survival
- Acceptance, understanding and support to make sense of things are key in supporting people who use self-harm

"I didn't stop overnight and I do not say I will never self-harm. I doubt very much I will but if I do then it will be because it will be necessary for my survival. There was no distinct recovery for me ...more a process that will continue until the day I die. A process of self-discovery and understanding...a process that is unique to me but something that every other human being is experiencing."

NB More information on CAPS and the motivation behind this chapter can be found in the appendices (1 and 2)

Bruce Wallace

References:
Scottish Recovery Network (SRN), www.scottishrecovery.net/What-is-Recovery/what-is-recovery.html

'Laurel'

Recovery...it is not as simple as the word sounds for something as complex as self-injury. If there was a fast, easy solution, I am sure most of us would take it, but the problem is, there is not a quick way to recover from something that is relied upon as a coping mechanism. Personally, I do not think it is possible to entirely recover from self-harm, however, I know that to be 'in recovery' or 'recovering' is certainly achievable because at present, I am in that stage. Hope does exist for those who self-injure; sometimes it just needs to be found.

I began self-harming three years ago, when I was sixteen, because I could not deal with the past and all the terrible memories that I was, and still am, dealing with. I was bullied, physically and emotionally, every day on the school bus from the age of eleven to about fifteen. I was called so many names, told I was worthless and that I should die, they threw my belongings everywhere, often hit me, dragged me onto the floor and once I was tied to the bus seat whilst one of the bullies attempted to set fire to me. I tried to block it all out because people say that if you ignore it, it will go away.

Sometimes, it just does not work like that though and sometimes, you just need to tell someone who can help put an end to the torment for you. Yet, this was only the beginning of my troubles, from the age of twelve I was also sexually abused by a family friend, which lasted until the age of sixteen, when I finally told my English teacher who along with the head of sixth form, informed my parents and ultimately, made sure it never happened again. However, the internal damage was already done and I continued to suffer with fear and guilt at having such terrifying memories inside of me. My overpowering hatred for myself could well be one of the main reasons I turned to self-injury.

At first, I did not realise that I had a problem, even though most of my day revolved around self-injury. Over the months, my self-injury became progressively worse and I did begin to understand I had a problem when I realised that I could not walk around without long sleeves on and I could never answer questions as to why I never took my jumper off. Of course, I was boiling in the summer, but I was too ashamed to reveal my self-injury. My Mum kept questioning me about this and showed a great deal of anger when she suspected me of hurting myself, although I denied the accusations continuously. But the pressure became overwhelming and I confided in my English teacher again.

My Mum was brought into school for a meeting with myself and the head of sixth form, where the news was broken.

One of the hardest parts of self-injury is the reaction that others have towards you. Often they mistake this coping mechanism for an act of attention seeking or even as stupidity, or they may see you as an 'emo'. These are all myths and in no way true. Do not let ignorant judgments silence you! My Mum, unfortunately, did not react sympathetically and refused to read anything to do with understanding self-injury. Instead, I received a considerable amount of anger and threats, which I had to face many more times after this too.

It is just hard when you cannot make somebody understand. I think to fully understand some things; you have to have been through similar situations yourself. That meeting was certainly not the end of my self-injury. For the past three years, I have been struggling to stop self- harming and each time I tried to stop, I soon started again. My self-harm continued to get worse, more dangerous. You see, it is a cycle, a vicious cycle that if you do not have the right support, will consume you with all of its power.

Contrastingly, there is always a turning point. A point where you realise that there is help available, and most importantly, there is hope. It may only be a small glimmer of light in the distance, but the second you begin to perceive it, you are a step closer and on the road to recovery. The depths of darkness can deceive you; it may make you believe that there is no such thing as recovery for those who self-injure. Sometimes you cannot find your way out of the maze of self-injury. But never give up because all you need is a map and then you are halfway there. The turning point for me was finding the help I so desperately needed from ChildLine; they gave me a regular counsellor who I spoke to every week for a few years and after working with her for some time, I started to see a tiny light at the end of the desperate darkness. ChildLine also gave me my best friend; we would never have found one another had it not been for our mutual link to ChildLine. To have someone who understands self-harm and who will always be there with you through the good times and the bad was the miracle that I had been wishing for since I was eleven.

Obviously, now I am no longer able to receive support from ChildLine, but they provided me with hope and with their and my best friend's previous help, I am currently well into recovering from self-injury. I have been free from it for nearly seven months now. To me, that is recovery. I cannot simply state that I have stopped for eternity, as self-injury does not work in that manner. You cannot predict what will happen in the future.

Recovery is not about that. Recovery is about finding other coping mechanisms, methods of expressing your feelings in a less dysfunctional way. I find drawing to be effective, it is the same sort of motion, and a release of what is inside you that perhaps cannot be expressed in words out loud. Writing helps, writing a rant about how you are feeling distracted me from self-harm or writing on your arms, maybe song lyrics that relate to the way you are feeling, or just words to express what is on the inside.

I have learnt not to let people tell me that recovery means you will never do it again. For someone who has suffered and continues to do so, that idea of never being able to access a coping mechanism again, puts too much pressure on that person. Pressure will only increase the risk of losing the ability to cope without self-injury.

Days must be taken one at a time. That is why every day I write down in my diary how many weeks/days I have been without self-harm. The more you see the days add up, the less chance you will have of losing the road to recovery. Of course, thoughts of self-injury do not disappear, they are always going to be present, but recovery means you are able to resist those ideas and distract yourself. If I suddenly have an urge to self-injure, I leave the room I am in and force myself to go out for a walk, with my music on, and let the fresh air wash over me. The angrier or more upset I am, the faster I walk. It is surprising how well this actually works. I have a butterfly book; it is where I keep all sorts of memories, inspirational quotes, pictures that mean things to me. When I am down, all the positive things that are so easily forgotten in the darkness are only a page away. So do not let somebody else determine what recovery is with their inaccurate judgments, it is personal to you.

Nowadays, I am studying for a degree in English Literature at University and my bedroom there is covered in everything butterfly related, the symbolism for freedom from self-injury. If someone asks me why I love butterflies, I am not afraid to tell them, for the scars on my arms are nothing to be ashamed of.

Recovery has enabled me to realise that and my aim will always be to promote awareness of self-injury so that those who suffer from it will be able to find the support and hope they need in order to recover too. Even if you do not believe it now, miracles do happen. Recovery taught me this. There is always a way out.

Bruce Wallace

Chapter 3

THE CONCEPT AND CHALLENGES OF RECOVERY FROM SELF-HARM IN THE PRISON POPULATION
Pras Ramluggun

- Introduction

The concept of recovery from self-harm in prison poses some challenges, which are inherent to the prison environment. It raises the question of whether a prison with high incidents of self-harm is an unhealthy prison. The notion of "unhealthy prison" has been coined by de Viggiani (2007, p1) who described prisons as agencies of disempowerment and deprivation. This view is supported by the Bradley et al (1998, p 50) argument that the Prison Service is "negative" and "barbaric" with regard to providing positive health. Therefore the approaches to support and empowering the prisoner to minimise self-harm based on the principles of engagement in the prison setting is a challenging endeavour.

The depiction of prison as a lonely and disempowering place further compounds the assiduous efforts to instil optimism and hope for the future. Despite these challenges there are some locally designed interventions and support by dedicated personnel in prison to support and help prisoners who self-harm. This chapter critically explores the occurrence of self-harm in prison and discusses some of the intrinsic challenges in supporting prisoners who self-harm. A deliberation on the potential solutions to overcome these barriers to enable prisoners to recover from self-harm are also offered.

- Definitional issues

When discussing self-harm it is imperative to clearly identify the phenomenon being examined, as there are definitional variances in the labelling and description of self-harm. It is an externalisation of an internal pain through direct or indirect bodily injury, which is unique to the person as a survival strategy with the intention to preserve life. Self-harm tends to describe broadly to encompass a range of self-inflicted harmful behaviour such as self-poisoning and self-mutilation (self-cutting, self-burning and self-biting) and self-strangulation. As not every means of self-harming is available in prisons, self-harm has been criticised as being an over-inclusive term in the prison context (Towl et al, 1999).

Nevertheless, it is the only term that is well recognised and acknowledged by almost everyone inside and outside prison.

Cutting with either accessible or improvised implements is the most common type of self-harm in prison. For the sake of clarity the act of self-harm relates to prisoners who harm themselves by the variety of means that are not culturally or socially sanctioned which are not considered to be direct attempts to end their lives. However, some prisoners may not intend to kill themselves, but in their desperate attempt to escape their distress their impulsive act of self-harm may have fatal consequences. These individuals tend to be labelled as self-harmers, which focuses on the problematic behaviour rather than the person behind the self-harm.

Self-harm has been identified as one of the most common problematic behaviours displayed by prisoners (Her Majesty's Inspectorate of Prisons for England and Wales, 2005) and up to 30% of prisoners in prisons in England and Wales have been reported to have a history of self-harm (Brooker at al, 2002). The proportion of female prisoners who self-harm is disproportionately high when compared with male prisoners in England and Wales (Ministry of Justice, 2012). This disproportion has been attributed to the vulnerability of female prisoners who are more likely to have had distressing life experiences as victims of abuse than male prisoners. However, self-harm is not exclusively a female phenomenon in prisons.

Self-harm is more likely to be noticed and detected in the close confinement of prison, but because of its ephemeral and secretive nature, the reported figures are not an accurate representation of self-harm incidents in prison.

Many factors have been associated with the aetiology of self-harm. The stress of incarceration can be a precursor for self-harm. In prison it is viewed as a subconscious escape for prisoners from their situation (Snow, 2002). The various theories, which try to explain how this multi-determined behaviour develops and is maintained, highlight its complexity. Although it is problematic to accurately predict which prisoner will exhibit self-harming behaviour, some factors have been associated with the susceptibility of some prisoners to engage in self-harm. These factors are explained in terms of either the location of the 'dis-ease' within the prisoner or the nature of the prison environment.

The adapted stress-vulnerability model devised by Zubin and Spring (1977, figure 1) demonstrates the vulnerability of people to stress. It describes how the individual's biological, psychological and social components shape their strengths and vulnerabilities while dealing with stress. The term vulnerability may appear to be value-laden, but the model tries to demonstrate vulnerability by identifying the variables involved in an individual's susceptibility to stress. When applied to the prison population it explains that the more difficulty that prisoners experience in adjusting to the prison regime, the more stress they experience and the more likely they are to resort to harmful behaviour (Snow, 2002). Bonner (1992, p 407), who used the model to explain prisoners' inability to cope with imprisonment potentially leading to suicide, stated that:

"...incarceration may bring about added stressors, such as loss of outside relationships, conflicts within the institution, victimization, further legal frustration, physical and emotional breakdown, and a wide variety of other problems in living. Coupled with such negative life stress, individuals with psychosocial vulnerabilities (including psychiatric illness, drug/alcohol intoxication, marital/ social isolation, suicidal coping history, and deficiencies in problem-solving ability) may be unable to cope effectively and in time may become hopeless."

Figure 1 Model of stress vulnerability (Adapted from Zubin & Spring, 1977)

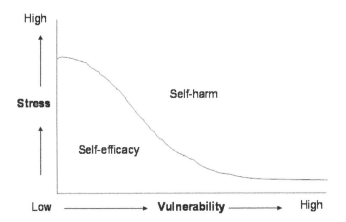

Kilty (2006) argues that viewing self-harm as primarily resulting from the individual limits the perspectives on this problematic behaviour to policies that focus solely on control and punishment, rather than embracing the broader context of this behaviour. The higher prevalence of self-harm in the prison population implies that there are contributory factors specific to prisons, which could be the prison environment, the prisoners or a combination of both.

The importation model suggests that prisoners' predisposition to self-harm stems from the behaviour patterns and values they brought into prison from the outside (Way et al, 2005; Wacquant, 2001). Spencer (2001, p18) argued that *"the seeds of poor health are sown for the majority long before they entered an institution",* with pre-existing health problems such as drug dependency and personality disorder (Marshall et al, 2000). The resistance or acquiescence to overwhelming prison conditions may depend on the individual's ability to cope.

A deficit in coping skills may contribute to the inability of some prisoners to adjust to the prison environment (Wichmann et al, 2002). Prisoners who self-harm share common features with the non- prison population and these are overrepresented in prison. They are a traumatic childhood, which includes a history of neglect, physical and sexual abuse (Crowe and Bunclark, 2000; Weaver et al, 2004), diagnosis of personality disorder (Klonsky et al, 2003), psychiatric illness and impairments such psychotic disorders, anxiety, depression and drug and alcohol dependency (Tripodi and Bender, 2007; Daniel and Flemming, 2006; Fruehwald et al, 2004).

Custodial characteristics such as remand prisoners (Loucks, 1998) and prisoners with long sentences and a history of violent offences (Ivanoff et al, 1996) have been associated with self-harm. However, a positive correlation does not mean that these are causative factors, as high functioning individuals with no underlying clinical diagnosis also self-harm (Klonsky, 2007).

Furthermore, prisoners with drug and alcohol addictions are at greater risk of self-harm and suicide during the withdrawal period and in the first few weeks after release from prison. One key recommendation of the Prison Service internal reviews on the prevention of suicide and self-harm in prison is that:

" The Prison Service should pay special attention to the safe management of prisoners in the early stages of custody in a prison, with a focus on excellence of care for all prisoners in reception, first night, induction and detoxification units." (HM Prison Service 2001, p 12)

The Sattar (2001) Report for the Home Office on the rates and causes of death among prisoners and offenders under community supervision emphasised the significant role played by alcohol and drugs in the violent death of community offenders. It reported that 10 per cent of all suicides/self-inflicted deaths occurred within one week of prisoners being released and 50 per cent within four weeks after release. It highlighted that the transition from prison into the community was a very risky time and recommended that policy initiatives for drug treatment through care

are needed to tackle such deaths both in prison and the community.

The Clinical Management of Drug Dependence in the Adult Prison Setting Report (Department of Health 2006, p 10) identified that the after-care package for prisoners with a substance misuse problem involve:

"access to additional support with a range of issues that may include housing, managing finance, rebuilding family relationships, learning new skills and employment. Early planning pre-release will enable continuity of care and access to wraparound support to be provided at the time when it is needed."

In the prison context, the relationship between self-harm and substance misuse is very much related. Prisoners struggling to cope with the physical and psychological effects of withdrawal symptoms from illicit drugs are likely to self-harm (Snow et al, 2003). Sixty percent of deaths occurring in the two weeks following release from prison were drug-related (Merrall et al, 2010). These drugs-related deaths amongst ex-prisoners were attributed to accidental drug overdose because they had a reduced tolerance to the toxic effects of opiates due to the periods of abstinence whilst in prison (Department of Health, 2006).

The white paper Tackling Drugs to build a Better Britain (Her Majesty's Government 1998, updated in 2008) and the Prison Service's Tackling drugs in prison (Her Majesty's Prison Service, 1998) strategies were set up to address these issues. Despite significant amounts of funding, these strategies have been criticised for lacking an evidenced knowledge base because research has mainly focused on drug users instead of other areas. This has resulted in resource allocation not being fully optimised (Howard, 2007).

- The debilitating nature of the prison environment

Linehan (1993) proposed that an invalidating environment where the language for expression of feelings was not validated, but instead reprimanded or trivialised, characterised those who self-harm. These individuals have no other way of articulating their needs and wishes compared to those who do not self-harm. In relation to the regulation of affect, research has shown that self-harming serves the function of enabling individuals to regain control over their overwhelming affective states (Nixon et al, 2002).

Goffman (1961, p 4) typified prison as a total institution where the deprivation of liberty is *"a barrier to social intercourse with the outside"* by being cut off from the outside world and where all aspects of life are integrated and governed by a set of prison rules. The deprivation theory posits that the maladaptation to prison conditions that deprives individuals of autonomy; liberty and security may lead to self-harm (Shalev, 2009; Berg and Delisi, 2006; Sykes, 1958).

The effect of deprivation can have a detrimental effect on the prisoner's physical, psychological and emotional wellbeing (Towl, 1999). Conditions of imprisonment linked to poor health cited in the literature include overcrowding, lack of meaningful activities, accessibility of illicit drugs, and experience of bullying, exploitation and exposure to violence (Howard League for Penal Reform, 2003; Croft, 2003; Levenson, 2002; Ireland, 2002; Toch, 1998).

Studies conducted by Dear et al (2001) indicated that the most common precipitating factor leading to self-harm was the stress of incarceration characterised by conflicts with other prisoners and prison staff (Travis and Waul, 2003). In such conflicts prisoners may also be forced to self-harm under duress although this is not openly or widely reported. The confines of the impersonal prison environment amplify the stressors of incarceration and limit the coping mechanisms, which may be available outside prison.

The authoritarian and controlling prison atmosphere, in addition to the fear of harm from other inmates, can contribute to a combined sense of poor personal worth, low self-esteem, embarrassment, shame, guilt and eventual loss of control over one's life (Roesch et al, 1998). In the words of Sykes (1958, p 79)

"the individual's picture of himself as a person of value, as an amorally acceptable, adult male who can represent some claim to merit in his material achievements and his inner strength begins to waver and grow dim."

Sociologists have identified several modes of adaptation to the prison regime. These can be narrowed down to either cooperating with the prison regime or resisting by withdrawing and keeping a low profile with a minimum degree of engagement and interaction with other inmates. The individuals who choose withdrawal are at most risk of self-destructive responses such as self-harm in order to regain control over their lives (Otto and Ogloff, 1988).

Based on Foucault's (1977) work on the exercise of disciplinary power in prison, Groves (2004) argued that self-harm can either be viewed as the outcome of an austere disciplinary regime of the prison where prisoners would either punish themselves or conversely, would use self-harm to resist such a regime by mobilizing much of the prison resources. The following statement by a prolific self-harming prisoner as cited in Fairall (1993, p 41) clearly illustrates this point:

"If I didn't like a particular situation or I thought there was something unjust I used my body as a hostage."

Foucault (1977, p 235-236) described prison as a *"complete and austere institution without exterior or gap with almost total power over the prisoners"*. However, prisons in England and Wales are becoming more open to outside agencies for the purpose of rehabilitation of prisoners and the provision of equitable healthcare, similar to that in the wider community. Therefore in addition to the power, authority and control that prison institutions have over prisoners they also have a legitimate responsibility for prisoners' welfare underpinned by a safer custody ethos.

- Intervention for self-harm in prison

McAllister et al (2002) remarked that despite all the information available on self-harm, this problematic behaviour remains a challenge to healthcare professionals. There is some evidence from hospital and community settings that structured programmes which teach problem-solving techniques may be useful in helping with the minimisation of self-harm (Hawton et al, 1998) and the principles of therapeutic community in some specialist prisons for prisoners with a personality disorder. Interventions which have had some success in managing self-harm include cognitive behavioural therapy, dialectical behaviour therapy (DBT) originally designed for chronically suicidal individuals, (Low et al, 2001) stress management, hypnotherapy (Aronowitz, 2001) and problem solving therapy (Muehlenkamp, 2006). DBT is a skills-based cognitive-behavioural group treatment with a focus on the interrelatedness of skills deficit (Linehan, 1993a).

Some of the structured programmes specifically tailored towards self-harm developed in prisons in England and Wales, incorporate elements from generic cognitive skills programme such as Stop and Think (McMurran et al, 2010) and the Enhanced Thinking Skills (McDougal et al, 2009). These programmes include the Carousel (HMP Brockhill), ACCESS (HMP Witherby), CHANGE (HMP Brixton), Alternatives to Self-Harm (HMP Holloway) and 'Help Me To Help Myself' (HMP Bristol).

Eccleston and Sorbello (2002) proposed the RUSH (real understanding of self-harm) Programme, a DBT-based intervention adapted from the work of Linehan (1993b). The practice of most of these programmes remains isolated in individual prison establishments and they are not rolled out throughout the Prison Service nationally or used to develop future services (Cutler, 1997).

According to the Samaritans, a UK-based voluntary support service for people at times of distress, prisoners in almost every UK prison have some form of access to their service and the emotional support it offers (Pollock et al, 2010). The Samaritans are widely welcome in the prison system to provide direct and indirect support to prisoners in partnership with HM Prisons in line with the Prison Service suicide and self-harm prevention strategy (Samaritans, 2010; HMP, 2008).

An indirect form of support for prisoners established by the Samaritans is the Listener's scheme, which offers training by local Samaritans to selected prisoners to become listeners to enable them to provide confidential support to fellow distressed prisoners. The Listener's scheme has been in operation in the UK prisons since 1991 when it was first piloted in HMP Swansea (Samaritans, 2011).

The Samaritans assert that they provide confidential and non-judgemental emotional support and adopt the position of self-determination where the caller is responsible for their own life (Samaritans, 2011). However, the issue of confidentiality and self-determination (unless it is face-to-face interactions where the volunteers are bound by law to seek medical help) poses ethical and legal problems in prison where prisoners' telephone calls are monitored and the Prison Service has a duty of care to all prisoners (Pollock et al, 2010; HMP, 2008).

The Prison Service Order 2700 stipulates that private access to the Samaritans should not be in conflict with the Prison Service and recommends that prisoners should have private access to a dedicated Samaritans telephone line (HMP, 2008).

Due to the dearth of studies on the effectiveness of the Listener's scheme there is no clear evidence about use of this strategy as a solution to self-harm in prison. This was recognised by the Head of operations at the Samaritans, who stated: "*Of course we can't prove that the listeners have reduced suicides or rates of self-harm*" (McVeigh, 2011 p1). Nevertheless, in their exploration of a similar scheme in operation in Canadian prisons, Hall and Gabor (2004) reported that this scheme was valuable to both prisoners and staff.

Dhaliwal and Harrower's (2009) evaluation of the impact of the scheme on listeners reported that it had a positive impact on them because they felt good about themselves by being able to help a fellow inmate. However, the evaluation did not look at the benefits for prisoners seeking help using the listener's scheme. Additionally as highlighted by Thackwray (2009), there are individuals who might choose to become listeners for their own individual gains in terms of their sentencing benefits. There are also others who are motivated to join the scheme to groom and abuse other prisoners. This underlines the importance of a robust screening and selection process for recruiting listeners to join the scheme.

Furthermore, the therapeutic community has demonstrated its effectiveness in the reduction of impulsive and self-harming behaviour in personality-disordered patients (Warren et al, 2006; Shuker and Newton, 2008). Although these therapeutic programmes are not specifically designed for those with personality disorders, it has been reported that some 88 % of prisoners referred to the 538 places in HMP Grendon, Dovegate, Gartree, Blundeston and Send (for women) prisons have a diagnosable personality disorder (Birtchnell and Shine, 2000). However, these prison-based therapeutic communities have been shown to be more effective for prisoners who have a degree of insight into their emotional difficulties and are able to receive and respond to feedback (Warren et al, 2003).

According to Shuker and Sullivan (2010), prison-based therapeutic community programmes such as those offered at HMP Grendon have been effective in modifying maladaptive interpersonal styles for personality-disordered prisoners. Compared to most prisons in England and Wales which adopt a traditionalist approach to disturbed behaviour such as adjudications and earned privileges for prisoners with good behaviour, HMP Grendon runs on a radically different basis with no such incentives (Inside Time, 2011). As a therapeutic community it embraces the principles of collaboration and participation based on a non-hierarchical environment with clear structure and boundaries where members are supported by each other and by staff and are given the opportunity to safely re-enact their past in order to better understand and deal with their problematic behaviours (Campling, 2001).

Despite housing a high population of prisoners with challenging behaviours, the incidence of self-harm has remained low at HMP Grendon (Her Majesty's Inspectorate of Prisons for England and Wales, 2007). This has been attributed to the environmental factors and the therapeutic programme (Shuker and Sullivan, 2010).

Self-harming behaviour needs to be recognized as an indicator of institutional morale, rather than solely as an individual's personal trouble (Hillbrand, 1993). Within the organisational system, management methods, multidisciplinary relationships, staff knowledge, beliefs and staff support have all been associated with positive attitudes to working with difficult and challenging behaviours (Ramluggun, 2013; Felce et al, 2000a). There is a dearth of studies on self-harm and suicide in prison staff. From

1990 to 2000, the number of reported prison staff who had killed themselves was 51.

After seven prison staff completed suicide in a single year in 1999, there were calls from the Prison Officers Association for urgent action to be taken. The Prison Officers' union chairman stated that:

> *"Budgetary constraints, together with new demands on performance-related targets, mean that prison officers are under more pressure than ever before. More money for occupational health and welfare is needed in order to tackle the problem. The Government could also help if it abandoned its plans to discipline staff who are simply off work ill."* (Waugh 2000, p 1)

Such support systems are therefore, paramount for those working closely with challenging behaviour like self-harm (Watts and Morgan, 1994; Reece, 2005). Burrow (1992, p 147) suggested that:

> *"Staff could be assisted by more theoretical knowledge and understanding of self-injurious motivations reinforced with in-service training, group discussions, clinical supervision, staff selection, staff procedures and an awareness of signs of burnout".*

- Risk management

Self-harm poses a challenge to any service but more so to the prison service because the interventions which aim to maintain the autonomy and control of the individual who self-harms are either unacceptable or perceived as inappropriate in prisons (Liebling, 1993). The Prison Service policy guideline for managing self-harm is underpinned by a prevention model, not well evidenced in contemporary literature (Pembroke, 2006). Hence the common approach to harm- minimisation in prison is limited to a prevention strategy that does not include safe self-harm practices. This is because acts of self-harm could result in accidental deaths and subsequent litigious actions.

The failure to protect the prisoner's life would be a breach of Article 2 of the Human Rights Act 1998, as set out in the European Convention on Human Rights which stipulates that: "*everyone's right to life shall be protected by law*" (Joint Committee on Human Rights 2004, p 1). Therefore, should the prisoner take his/her own life whilst under the care of the prison authorities, the latter could be held liable for the death of the prisoner under this Convention. This is in addition to the domestic law of negligence if it can be proved that the duty of care owed to the prisoner has been broken (Foster, 2009). Hence, a damage limitation approach, which focuses on the expression of self-harm rather than the person exhibiting the behaviour, is preferred (Harris, 2000; Babiker and Arnold, 1998).

Pembroke (2006) argued that for individuals who self-harm, the survival value of the behaviour needs to be recognised. However, the implementation of a harm-minimisation approach needs careful planning and support from the organisation (Pengelly et al, 2008). Similar to suicide, it is not illegal to self-harm. However, this does not mean that individuals are entitled to inflict harm on themselves as they wish.

The State has a general duty to protect its citizens in prisons and wider society, which includes preventing individuals from harming themselves with laws such as the ban on the use of illicit drugs. In cases where the severity of the self-harm may be potentially fatal the rights to protect the individual can override the latter's choice to exhibit such behaviour especially when there is no suicidal intent. Kennedy and Grubb (1998) cited the use of common law to save the patient's life in circumstances where competence cannot be clearly established and where the patient's life is threatened by the act of self-harm.

The issue of the prisoners' rights to self-harm is important as it poses practical difficulties and ethical dilemmas. On the one hand the Prison Service has an obligation to keep the prisoner safe by stopping the latter from self-harming and yet prisoners would argue for the right to harm themselves as they wish without interference. If the self-destructive act is not underscored by a diagnosable mental illness and the prisoner is deemed to have decision-making capacity, this raises the question of the prisoner's absolute autonomy over his or her body.

If the self-harming behaviour is not a lethal act and does not put others at risk of harm, the Prison Service intervention to stop the prisoner from self-harming can be perceived as an interference with the prisoner's right to self-determination. The compelling interest in what a prisoner does to his or her body when there is no fatal outcome and no intention of direct harm to others is questionable under the harm principle, which states that:

> "The only purpose for which power can be exercised over any member of a civilised community, against his will is to prevent harm to others. His own good, either physical or moral is not a sufficient warrant. He cannot rightfully be compelled to do or forbear because it will be better for him to do so, because it will make him happier, because, in the opinions of others, to do so would be wise or even right" (Mill, 1859 p1).

At the heart of this debate lies the fundamental question whether the right to life supersedes all other rights. The Prison Service has stressed that it does not sanction the act of safe self-harm (HMPS, 2007). Paradoxically the Prison Service is also reluctant to restrict access to readily available implements that could be used to self-harm in order to avoid potential litigation, even though these measures could be justified as necessary to maintain prisoners' safety (Batty, 1998).

There is a fear that such action would constitute a breach of prisoners' human rights. Thus, the ambiguity of the Prison Service's standpoint on the management of self-harm lies in the degree of responsibility for the self-harming behaviour. It could also be argued that in the absence of liberty the degree of responsibility cannot be fully exercised by prisoners.

The use of the strategy of safe self-harm in prison in promoting the individual's autonomy whereby the individual may be provided with the means to self-harm with the aim of minimising suicide risk and reducing the risk of serious injury has not received much debate. Due to the controversy surrounding this practice clear guidelines informed by philosophical ethical and practical debate is needed to ensure its efficacy in the prison setting.

Hassan et al (1999) stressed that the management of self-harm in patients who refuse treatment is a complex issue. They argued that there is a lack of clarity on how clinicians should proceed and proposed an algorithm to guide practice in this area. Edwards and Hewitt (2011) advocate for a supervised approach to self-harm including strategies to reduce self-harm to prevent the individual becoming conditioned to this behaviour.

- Interdisciplinary conflicts

The challenges of managing self-harm are compounded when working across perspectives and are dependent on the concepts, theories and beliefs that one uses to process and structure information. According to Dales and Woods (2001, p19) the unique culture of the prison can test the *"moral and ethical working practices of clinicians".* Studies on the views of self-harm by staff working in prison indicated differences in perception both within and across the various disciplines and departments involved in the management of prisoners who self-harm.

The differences ranged from the causes and purpose of the act of self-harm (Dickinson and Wright, 2009) to the severity of the injury to the repetitiveness of the act (Ramluggun, 2013; Pannell et al, 2003; Short et al, 2009). The ambiguity of prison officers about their roles and the lack of support and training to deal with self-harm have also been reported (Ramluggun, 2013; Short et al, 2009). Consequently, differences of opinion between clinicians and prison officers on what would best serve the wellbeing of prisoners are evident (Ramluggun, 2013; Short et al, 2009; Sim, 2002). The contentious toleration of healthcare staff by custodial staff can impact on the correctional healthcare environment (Droes, 1994). This point can be further illustrated in the field of forensic mental health, where clinicians have to balance therapeutic practice with the need for security (Polczyk-Prybyla and Gournay, 1999). In prisons, clinicians have to balance the restrictive boundaries imposed by the Prison Service for the safeguard of the public with the fundamentals of initiating and maintaining a caring relationship with prisoners.

The cognitive challenges of collaborative working between healthcare and the Prison Service personnel on self-harm have not been given prominence. This is evidenced by the lack of prioritising of resources and the lack of evidence-based service provision in the Bradley's Report (Department of Health, 2009). The social identity theory postulates that the attitudes and behaviour of members of one group towards the other depends on the members' professional identity (Haslam et al, 2001). How the group members compare and differentiate themselves from another group depends on the context and which identity is more salient. The focal task of the prison is dictated by the public's general opinion, which views security as the major responsibility of the prison. Hence, Mental Health Professionals (HMPs) working in prisons occupy a delicate position and their decision-making process for the management of prisoners who self-harm is predetermined by the dominant prison personnel's identity.

The predominantly prison focused tool the assessment, care and custody and teamwork (ACCT) document needs reviewing and changes in how this document is implemented. The shift in the thinking for how the ACCT could be better implemented needs to be informed by regular reflective practice on supporting prisoners who exhibit self-harming behaviour taking into account the views of all staff involved.

- Conclusion

There is no straight and single answer for recovery from self-harm, which is recognised as *"an enormously difficult behaviour to manage and work with"* (WHO, 2000 p11) in prison. This task is made more arduous when the environment has been designed primarily for punishment, correction and potentially for the rehabilitation of prisoners. It is apparent that there is a paradigm shift in the thinking and mainstream approaches in how to respond to self-harm. Studies have also shown that there is a causal relationship between staff perceptions and their willingness to help. Hence, there is an emerging consensus in mainstream services to focus on innovative practice by exploring new ways of working with individuals who self-harm. Although the notion of a healthy prison and a progressive healthcare system continues to evolve and influences how prisoners are treated, innovative approaches to helping prisoners who exhibit self-harming behaviour has not received much debate where the model of prevention of self-harm prevails.

The overriding authority of the Prison Service over the management of prisoners can lead to an unequal balance in the decision-making process on the care and treatment of prisoners who self-harm. Therefore, the complex interlocking structures between the prison and healthcare, and the dialectical relationship and position of power of these two systems makes the care management of self-harm within this 'captive' population more challenging. Concerted effort is required on both sides to critically appraise this multi-determined phenomenon and the multidimensional approaches required in managing its complexity.

The determination to strive to collectively manage this phenomenon in prison should take into account the intricacies of practices, which is underscored by the inherent tensions that are evident amongst clinicians and prison staff for a best practice model. The appropriateness of the roles of both healthcare and the prison service staff in collectively managing this phenomenon would require all concerned to consider their own values and beliefs, legal and ethical aspects of their duties to prisoners who self-harm.

References:

Babiker G., and Arnold L. (1998), The Language of Injury. BPS Blackwell Books, London.

Batty D. (1998), Coping by Cutting. Nursing Standard, Vol. 12 (29) pp. 24-25.

Berg M., and DeLisi M. (2006), The correctional melting pot: Race, ethnicity, citizenship, and prison violence, Journal of Criminal Justice, Vol. 34 (6) pp.631-642.

Birtchnell J., and Shine J. (2000), Personality disorders and the interpersonal octagon. British Journal of Medical Psychology, Vol. 73 pp.433–448.

Bonner R. L. (1992), "Isolation, Seclusion, and Psychological Vulnerability as Risk Factors for Suicide Behind Bars. Assessment and Prediction of Suicide. New York, NY: Guilford Press.

Brooker C., Repper J., Berverley C., Ferriter M., and Brewer M. (2002), Mental Health Services and Prisoners: A Review. School of Health and Related Research. University of Sheffield.

Bradley G., Hastings D., and Niland L. (1998), Healing the Offender, Prison Service Journal, Vol. 3 pp.50-53.

Burrow S. (1992), The deliberate self-harming behaviour of patients within a British special hospital, Journal of Advanced Nursing, Vol. 17 pp.138-148.

Campling P. (2001), Therapeutic Communities. Advances in psychiatric Treatment, Vol. 7 pp.365–372.

Croft J. (2003), Human Rights and Public Authorities. A Report prepared for the Joint Committee on Human Rights, Chapter 74, London: The Prison Reform Trust.

Crowe M., and Bunclark J. (2000), Repeated self-injury and its management. International Review of Psychiatry, Special Issue: Suicide and Attempted Suicide, Vol. 12 pp.48–53.

Cutler J., Bailey J., and Dexter P. (1997), Suicide awareness training for prison staff: An evaluation. Issues in Criminological and Legal Psychology, Vol. 28 pp.65-69.

Dales C., and Woods P. (2001), Caring for prisoners: RCN Prison Nurses Forum. Roles and Boundaries Project. Royal college of Nursing, London.

Daniel A.E., and Flemming J. (2006), Suicides in a state correctional system 1992-2002. Journal of correctional Health Care, Vol. 12 pp.24-35.

Dear G. E., Thompson D. M., Howells K., and Hall J. G. (2001), Non-fatal self-harm in Western Australian prisons: Who, when, where and why? Australian and New Zealand Journal of Criminology, Vol. 34 pp. 47-66.

Department of Health. (2006), Clinical Management of Drug Dependence in the Adult Prison Setting. Including Psychosocial Treatment as a Core Part, Department of Health Publications London.

Department of Health. (2009), The Bradley's report. London: Department of Health Publications Orderline.

de Viggiani N. (2006), Surviving prison: exploring prison social life as a determinant of health, International Journal of Prisoner Health, Vol. 2(2) pp.71–89.

Dhaliwal R., and Harrower J. (2009), Reducing prisoner vulnerability and providing a means of empowerment: evaluating the impact of a Listener Scheme on the Listeners. British Journal of Forensic Practice, Vol. 11(3) pp.35-43

Dickinson T., and Wright K.M. (2009), The attitudes of nursing staff in secure environments to young people who self-harm. Journal of Psychiatric and Mental Health Nursing, Vol. 16 (10) pp.947–951.

Droes N. S. (1994), Correctional Nursing Practice, Journal of Community Health Nursing, Vol. 11 (4) pp.201-210.

Eccleston L., and Sorbello L. (2002), The RUSH program — real understanding of self-help: a suicide and self-harm prevention initiative within a prison setting. Australian Psychologist, Vol. 37 (3) pp.237-244.

Fairall P. (1993), Violent Offenders and Community Protection in Victoria - The Gary David experience. Criminal Law Journal, Vol. 17 pp. 40-54.

Felce D., Bowley C., Baxter H., Jones E., Lowe K., and Emerson E. (2000a), The effectiveness of staff support: evaluating Active Support training using a conditional probability approach. Research in Developmental Disabilities, Vol. 21 pp.243-255.

Foster S. (2009), Prison Conditions and Human Rights: the development of judicial protection of prisoners' rights. Web Journal of Current Legal Issues. Retrieved on 14.12.2011 from http://webjcli.ncl.ac.uk/2009/issue1/foster1.html.

Fruehwald S., Matsching T., Koenig F., Bauer P., and Frottier P. (2004), Suicide in custody. A case control study. British Journal of Psychiatry, Vol. 185 pp.494-498.

Foucault M. (1977), Discipline and Punish: the Birth of the Prison. London: Allen Lane.

Goffman E. (1961), Asylums. Harmondsworth: Penguin Books.

Groves A. (2004), Blood on the walls: Self-mutilation in prisons. New Zealand Journal of Criminology, Vol. 37 pp.49–64.

Hassan T.B,   MacNamara A.F., Davy A., Bing A., and Bodiwala G.G. (1999), Managing patients with deliberate self-harm who refuse treatment in the accident and emergency department. British Medical Journal, Vol. 319 pp.107-109.

Harris J. (2000), Self-harm: Cutting the bad out of me. Qualitative Health Research, Vol. 10 (2) pp.164-173.

Haslam A. S. (2001), Psychology in Organizations - The Social Identity Approach, London: Sage Publications Ltd.

Her Majesty's Inspectorate of Prison for England and Wales. (2007), The Mental Health of Prisoners. A thematic review of the care and support of prisoners with mental health needs Department of Health, London.

Her Majesty's Prison Service. (2001), Prevention of Suicide and Self-Harm in the Prison Service: An Internal Review. London: HM Prison Service.

Her Majesty's Inspectorate of Prisons for England and Wales. (2005), Annual Report of Her Majesty's Chief Inspector of Prisons for England and Wales (2004-2005). London: The Stationery Office.

Her Majesty's Prison Service. (2008), Prison Service Order 2700. Suicide Prevention and Self-Harm Management. Issue 283. Ministry of Justice London.

Hillbrand M. (1993), Self-injurious behaviour in correctional and non-correctional psychiatric patients. Journal of Offender Rehabilitation, Vol. 19 pp.95-102

Howard League for Penal Reform. (2003), Suicide and self-harm prevention. The management of self-injury in prison. The Howard League. London.

Howard P. (2007), Between the lines. New drug strategies must reflect changing consumption patterns. Retrieved on 14.06.2011 from:
http://www.guardian.co.uk/society/2007/apr/18/drugsandalcohol.comment

Inside Time. (2011), HMP Grendon Prison Regime. Retrieved on 11.06.2011 from: http://www.insidetime.org/info-regimes2.asp?nameofprison=HMP_GRENDON

Ireland J.L. (2002), Bullying among prisoners: Evidence, Research and intervention strategies, London, UK: Brunner-Routledge.

Ivanoff A., Jang S. J., and Smyth N. J. (1996), Clinical risk factors associated with parasuicide in prison. Journal of Offender Therapy Comparative Therapy, Vol. 40 (2) pp.135-146.

Kennedy I., and Grubb A. (1998), Principles of Medical Law. Oxford: Oxford University Press

Kilty J.M. (2006), Under the barred umbrella: Is there room for a women-centred self-injury policy in Canadian corrections? Criminology & Public Policy.

Klonsky D., Oltmanns T. F., and Turkheimer E. (2003), Deliberate Self-Harm in a Nonclinical Population: Prevalence and

Psychological Correlates. American Journal of Psychiatry, Vol. 160 (8) pp.1501-1508.

Klonsky E.D. (2007), The functions of deliberate self-injury. A review of the evidence. Clinical Psychology Review, Vol. 27, pp.226-239.

Levenson J. (2002), Prison Overcrowding: The inside Story. Britain: Prison Reform Trust.

Loucks N. (1998), HMPI Corton Vale. Research into drugs and alcohol, violence and bullying, suicides and self-injury and backgrounds of abuse. Scottish Prison Service occasional papers, 1/98.

Liebling A. (1993), Suicide attempts and self-injury in male prisons. Great Britain Home Office. London.

Linehan M. M. (1993a), Cognitive-behavioural treatment of borderline personality disorder. New York: Guilford.

Linehan M.M. (1993b), Skills training manual for treating borderline personality disorder. New York: Guilford.

Low G., Jones D., and Duggan C. (2001), The treatment of deliberate self-harm in borderline personality disorder using dialectical behaviour therapy: A pilot study in high security hospital. Behavioural and Cognitive Psychotherapy, Vol. 29 pp.85-92.

Marshall T., Simpson S., and Stevens A. (2000), Health Care in Prisons: A Health Needs Assessment, Edgbaston: University of Birmingham.

McMurran M., Huband N., and Overton E. (2010), Non-completion of personality disorder treatments: A systematic review of correlates, Consequences and interventions. Clinical Psychology Review, Vol. 30 pp.277-287.

McAllister M., Creedy D., Moyle W., and Farrugia C. (2002), Nurses' attitudes towards clients who self-harm. Journal of Advanced Nursing Vol. 40 (5) pp.578-586.

Merrall E.L., Kariminia A., Binswanger I.A., Hobbs M.S., Farrell M., Marsden J., Huchinson S.J., and Bird S.M. (2010), Meta-analysis of drug-related deaths soon after release from prison. Addiction Review. Retrieved on 12.06.2011from
http://onlinelibrary.wiley.com/doi/10.1111/j.1360-0443.2010.02990.x/pdf

Mill J.S. (1859), On liberty. In Philosophy of Law (2010) pp. 1-3. Retrieved on 10.05.2011 from available from http://carneades.pomona.edu/2010-Law/hdo-0331.pdf

Ministry of Justice. (2012), National Offender Management Service. Estate Planning and Development Unit. Prison population and accommodation briefing for 09/02/2009. Retrieved on 10.02.2012 from: http://www.hmprisonservice.gov.uk/resourcecentre

Muehlenkamp J. (2006), Empirically supported treatments and general therapy guidelines for non-suicidal self-injury. Journal of Mental Health Counselling, Vol. 28 (2) pp. 166-185.

Nixon M., Cloutier P., and Aggarwal S. (2002), Affect Regulation and Addictive Aspects of Repetitive Self-Injury in Hospitalized Adolescents. Journal of the American Academy of Child & Adolescent Psychiatry, Vol. 41(11) pp.1333–1340.

Otto R.K., and Ogloff J.R.P. (1988), A manual for Mental Health Professionals working with Jails. Lincoln NE: Nebraska Department of Public Institution.

Pannell J., Kevin H., and Andrew Day. (2003), Prison Officers' Beliefs Regarding Self-Harm in Prisoners: An Empirical Investigation. International Journal of Forensic Psychology, Vol. 1 (1) pp.103-110.

Pengelly N., Ford B., Blenkiron P., and Reilly S. (2008), Harm minimisation after repeated self-harm: development of a trust handbook. Psychiatric Bulletin, 32 pp.60-63.

Pembroke L. (2006), Offer us what we want. Mental Health Today, pp.16–18.

Pollock K., Armstrong S., Coveney C., and Moore J. (2010), An Evaluation of Samaritans Telephone and Email Emotional Support Service. The National Institute for Health Research/ University of Nottingham.

Polczyk-Prybyla M., and Gournay K. (1999), Psychiatric nursing in prison: the state of the art? Journal of Advanced Nursing, Vol. 30 (4) pp. 893-900.

Power K., McElroy J., and Swanson V. (1997), Coping abilities and prisoners' perception of suicidal risk management. The Howard Journal, Vol. 36 pp.378-392

Ramluggun P. (2013), A Critical Exploration of the Management of Self-Harm in a Male Custodial Setting: Qualitative Findings of A Comparative Analysis of Prison Staff Views on Self-Harm. Journal of Forensic Nursing. 1 (9) pp.23-34

Reece J. (2005), The language of cutting. Initial reflections on a study of the experiences of self-injury in a group of women and nurses. Issues in Mental Health Nursing, Vol. 26 pp.561-574.

Roesch R., Ogloff R. P., Zapf P. P. A., Hart S. D., and Otto R. (1998), Mental health issues for jail and prison inmates: A review of prevalence, assessment, and treatment. In N. Singh (Ed.), Comprehensive clinical psychology: Applications in diverse populations (pp. 89-104). Oxford, Elsevier.

Samaritans. (2010), Reports highlights increase in self-harm. Retrieved on 01.12.2010 from: http://www.samaritans.org/media_centre/emotional_health_news/n hs_self_harm-057-1-1-2.aspx

Samaritans. (2011), Our work in prisons. Retrieved on 20.05.2011from:
http://www.samaritans.org/your_emotional_health/our_work_in_pris ons.aspx

Sattar G. (2001), Rates and causes of death among prisoners and offenders under community supervision. Home Office Research Study 231. Home Office Research, Development and Statistics Directorate.

Shalev S. (2009), Inside a Supermax. Prison Service Journal, Vol. 181(1) pp.21-25.

Short V., Cooper J., Shaw J., Abel K., Kenning C., and Chew-Graham C. (2009), Custody vs care: attitudes of prison staff to self-harm in women prisoners - a qualitative study. The Journal of Forensic Psychiatry & Psychology, Vol. 20 (3) pp.408–426.

Shuker R., and Newton M. (2008), Treatment outcome following intervention in a prison-based therapeutic community: A study of the relationship between reduction in criminogenic risk and improved psychological wellbeing. British Journal of Forensic Practice. Vol. 10 (3) pp.33-44

Shuker R., and Sullivan E. (2010), Grendon and the Emergence of Forensic Therapeutic Communities. Chichester: John Wiley & Sons.

Sim J. (2002), The future of prison health care: a critical analysis. Critical Social Policy, Vol. 22 (2) pp.300-323.

Spencer A. (2001), 'Removing bars to good treatment.' NHS Magazine.

Snow L. (2002), Prisoners motives for self-injury and attempted suicide. British Journal of Forensic practice, Vol. 4 (4) pp.18-29.

Snow L., Greenaway B., and Paton J. (2003), "Report of the F213 Self-harm Data Collection project: Summary of key findings. Safer Custody Newsletter, HM Prison Service. HMSO.

Sykes G.M. (1958), The Society of Captives. A study of a maximum security prison. Princeton: Princeton University Press.

Thackwray A. (2009), Are you still listening? Listener Screening and Selection. Retrieved on 06/01/2012 from:
http://www.insidetime.org/articleview.asp?a=543&c=are_you_still_li stening_listener_screening_and_selection

Toch H. (1998), Hypermasculinity and prison violence. Bowker, L.H. (ed.) Masculinities and Violence. London: Sage Publications.

Towl G. J., McHugh M. J., and Jones D. (1999), Suicide in Prisons: Research, Policy and Practice. Brighton: Pavilion Publishing.

Travis J., and Waul M. (2003), Prisoners once removed. The impact of incarceration and re-entry on children, families and communities of prisoners. Urban University Press Washington.

Tripodi S. J., and Bender K. (2007), Inmate Suicide: Prevalence, Assessment, and Protocols. Brief Treatment and Crisis Intervention, Vol. 7(1) pp.40-54.

Wacquant L. (2001), 'Deadly Symbiosis: When Ghetto and Prison Meet and Mesh', Punishment & Society, Vol. 3 (1) pp.95–134.

Wichmann C., Serin R., and Abracen J. (2002), Women prisoners who engage in self-harm: A comparative investigation. Ontario, Canada: Correctional Service of Canada Research Branch.

Warren F., Preddy-Fayers K., and McGauley G.I. (2003), Review of Treatments for Severe Personality Disorder. London: Home Office Online Publication.

Warren F., Evans C., and Dolan B. (2006), Impulsivity and self-damaging behaviour in severe personality disorder: The impact of democratic therapeutic community treatment. The International Journal of Therapeutic Communities and Supportive Organisations, Vol. 25 pp. 55-71.

Watts D., and Morgan H.G. (1994), Malignant alienation. Dangers for patients who are hard to like. British Journal of Psychiatry, Vol. 164 pp. 11-15.

Waugh P. (2000), Jail union seeks action to cut high staff suicide rate. Retrieved on 11.01.2012 from: http://www.independent.co.uk/news/uk/this-britain/jail-union-seeks-action-to-cut-high-staff-suicide-rate-710823.html

Way B.B., Miraglia R., Sawyer D.A., Beer R., and Eddy J. (2005), Factors related to suicide in New York State prisons. International Journal of Law and Psychiatry Vol. 28 pp.207-221.

World Health Organisation. (2000), Preventing suicide: A resource for prison officers. Geneva: WHO.

Zubin J., and Spring B. (1977), Vulnerability - a new view of schizophrenia. Journal of Abnormal Psychology Vol. 86 (2) pp.103-124.

Bruce Wallace

'John'

My name is John and I am a 28 year-old male. It is difficult to know where to start this story but I suppose some general information might help. I grew up in what I consider a 'normal' family with a mum, dad and older brother. My family were (and still are) close and we spent a lot of time doing 'family things' like shopping, watching television, playing card games. We also went on regular holidays together to places like the seaside here in the UK and enjoyed all the British weather had to offer in a typical summer!

My brother and I played with many of the other local kids on the council estate where we grew up. The only issue I could really think of in my early childhood was one of being quite shy and self-conscious. I found it hard to make friends and at school would watch as others played together and although I desperately wanted to join in couldn't get up the courage to ask. I found this both frustrating and a little worrying and wondered if there was something wrong with me. One or two of the other kids also used to pick on me but it wasn't too bad and a number of other kids had their share of this too.

I found it hard to express how I was feeling and often found myself feeling annoyed and getting frustrated and angry at minor things without having any real way to deal with them. I occasionally vented this anger on inanimate objects by breaking them but only if there was no one around at the time.

When I moved to secondary school at 11 the situation became worse as the school was much larger and somewhat overwhelming with lots of different classes to attend and new children most of whom I didn't know. I tended to keep myself to myself and made no real friends in any of the classes I was in. My mum would ask me frequently how things were going when I got home and I would just say the usual about everything going fine to avoid having to say how I was actually feeling.

Other kids around appeared more confident, mature and knowledgeable compared to me. They could talk to other quite easily and when it came to members of the opposite sex they seemed to know what to say to them and I had no idea and was frightened of saying something stupid. I can remember going to a school dance close to Christmas when I was about 12 and one girl came over and asked me to dance. I was both excited and terrified at the same time and quietly refused because I was so embarrassed and also worried about making a fool of myself. She went and asked someone else of course and this left me feeling both frustrated and rejected. I spent the rest of the evening sitting in a corner trying to avoid any chance of someone coming to talk to me or maybe even asking for a dance.

Later that evening when I got home having avoided any awkward answers to my mum's questions about how everything had gone, I went upstairs to my room. I remember playing about with a hobby knife that I had for making small wooden models and I suddenly realized that I had cut my arm and that it was bleeding. It was painful but also strangely soothing; I realized that the frustration I had been feeling had been forgotten during the time that I had been thinking about what I had just done and the pain that accompanied it. Afterwards I covered the cut in case anyone saw it and asked any awkward questions and then thought little more about it.

This was my first introduction to self-harming and it was to become a regular part of my life. I had no real idea why I did it and didn't know anyone else who did so I just quietly relied on it when issues became too overwhelming for me to deal with. It helped me to deal with the frustration and anger of being a young adult but feeling like a child compared to my peers. They all appeared to know more than me and be more mature than me (both physically and emotionally). The physical aspect was particularly embarrassing in communal changing areas before and after sports days where it was hard to avoid seeing other naked bodies and when compared to me they all appeared to be 'grown up' whereas I wasn't or thought I wasn't.

I didn't know how to ask anyone why I appeared to be different and when this became something that would make me feel angry at myself and others I dealt with the issue by cutting. It didn't help my concerns regarding my being different but reduced the level of frustration that I could feel beginning to build up. I thought at one point of talking to a teacher who was quite human and approachable but they were busy at that point in time and the moment passed and I didn't try again. The added pressure of examination preparation began and the 'a good education equals a good job' comments from well-meaning parents only added to the overall feeling of being overwhelmed. I had by now been self-harming for about three years and it was an integral part of my lifestyle; if I had a bad day or was feeling particularly stressed then I would cut in the privacy of my room and feel better but this came at a price. I had to be careful to tidy up afterwards and to ensure that there was no evidence of what I had been doing. I also had to avoid wearing any short sleeved shirts or t-shirts so that no one would ask any potentially awkward questions. There was also a strange feeling of guilt linked to the self-harming as I somehow recognized that it was something I shouldn't really be doing but couldn't stop at this point. It helped me feel better at times but also made me feel guilty and a little ashamed, something I found difficult to deal with. It was almost like a coin with two sides; one good, one not so good.

I spent less time harming during the time spent studying for GCSE's as I had something to preoccupy me and it also allowed me less time to think about anything that might make me too frustrated or anxious. After the exams had finished and the results were published I was surprised that I had managed to do quite well – enough to go to university if I wanted to. Again the thought of another change arose and I started to become anxious about leaving school and going somewhere different. My parents were very pleased at the thought of university and encouraged me as my older brother had left school quite early and gone to work in a local garage and I would represent the family as the first one to go to university.

I had to complete the various forms and visited several universities with my mum, finally settling on one that appeared to be quite suitable (i.e. seemed quite friendly and not too far away from where I lived). I was now self-harming less frequently than I had been at school but occasionally resorted to it when things became too stressful or my frustration at my own inadequacies bubbled to the surface. Self-harm was always available and was used almost as a distraction when any situation became too difficult so was quite random in how often it was needed.

When I first started university life was quite good. I had moved into student accommodation and found that the social life there was good, particularly after I had a few drinks. I had just discovered the 'cure' for my inadequacy and frustration and it was called alcohol. Unfortunately it also helped to speed up my need to self-harm if things did not go well. If I felt alone, rejected, angry, or anxious then after a few drinks I found myself cutting back in my room. At the time I did not link the two; this only came later.

At about this time I met and managed to talk to a female student one evening after a few drinks. This was actually the first time I had the courage to 'chat up' a female and I was now 18 years old! I am not sure that she was overly impressed but she did at least agree to meet me again. This was the beginning of the best and worst time of my life to that point. After a few dates we were beginning to become a couple but I still needed a drink to be sociable and it did not go unnoticed by her. After one particular evening out she asked me why I always seemed to 'need' a drink to talk to anyone including her – was there a problem? I struggled to provide a reasonable answer and ended up feeling quite inadequate, getting angry and then stormed off. After getting back to my room I reached for a sharp knife and cut myself but ended up cutting more deeply than I had intended. I was trying to stop the bleeding when she turned up at my door. Unable to think of an excuse and not wanting to avoid her in case she decided to leave I couldn't think of anything else and ended up opening the door and just standing there.

She looked at me and then at the blood that was running from the wound on my arm and asked me what had happened. I blurted out what I had done and why and found myself suddenly talking about everything including my self-harming. It was like a tap had been turned on and I couldn't stop until I had finished telling her everything. She just listened quietly until I had finished and then gave me a hug. I started crying; this isn't what was supposed to happen – men are meant to give a woman a hug when they cry not the other way round! When I had finally finished talking and crying she sat me down and told me that she had heard about people who self-harmed but hadn't suspected me. She said she had been more worried about my drinking and was concerned about that and how I occasionally behaved after a few drinks. We spent most of the rest of the night talking and in the morning I promised to contact the support services at the university and make an appointment to talk to someone.

As I mentioned before, the worst time was hurting someone I cared about very much and then having to explain to them what until then had been my secret life. The best time was her reaction and acceptance of me as an individual and amusingly her concern about my drinking rather than my self-harm! I followed up my promise to go to the university support services and an appointment was made for me to see a counsellor. As a result of the time spent with this person I have subsequently learned how to deal more constructively with my feelings, particularly those related to frustration and anxiety. Alcohol is now a limited part of my life and not used as a way of compensating for my inadequacies. I now realize that much of what I was feeling was quite 'normal' but I hadn't had the confidence to explore this and maybe ask other people and find this out.

I haven't self-harmed since that night that my girlfriend discovered what I had been doing. The shock of what I had done and the long talk that we had helped me to make the changes needed. I was able to ask for help and this helped me to find an explanation that made sense to me regarding how I had been feeling and why I turned to self-harm at certain times in my life. It surprises me now that I was able to stop so suddenly. I had started to read some of the material available and some of it indicated that self-harming could become quite addictive. It also stated in some leaflets that I was given that it was important for me to decide when the time was right. It must have been right on that particular night!

I am now quite confident that I am unlikely to need to self-harm again; my life is good at this moment. My girlfriend is now my wife and I have many things to look forward to. I am not stupid and am aware that there will be times where things might be difficult but I am confident that I now have a collection of strategies that I can use other than self-harming to deal with them. Does this then mean that I have recovered? I am not sure that the word is really appropriate; I would prefer to say that my life is more positive and that this will continue – sounds better!

Bruce Wallace

'Natalie'

I haven't cut since November of last year. Last night I had a thought though. I wanted to cut, because I literally felt like NOTHING. Not in terms of self-worth, but in terms of emotion. I felt absolutely nothing. I was laying in bed and just thinking about this feeling, and all of a sudden I started biting my hand until marks were left that would last a couple of hours.

I did it because I wanted to feel, and I have never cut for this reason. It was always for release. That was the first time I have ever felt this way. There were scissors in my drawer and I got them and felt the edges, reminding me of 'old times', but I didn't use them for three reasons.

1. I am very picky with what I use,
2. I was already feeling a bit of pain from my hand so I wanted to 'save the cutting for later', and probably the most important reason is
3. It didn't feel worth it.

I didn't WANT to relapse. I didn't want to say 'I cut myself'. I want to be a RECOVERED self-harmer. And I will stay that way. No matter how tempting this is, I will make sure of it.

Just thought I'd say this

Bruce Wallace

Chapter 4
RECOVERY AND SELF-HARM: REFLECTIONS ON A PERSONAL JOURNEY
'J'

What is recovery? What does it mean?

For me, recovery has been an extended journey in which I have strived to find a way in which I can live with myself, the unknown elements that life brings, my decisions, and their consequences, without feeling the overwhelming need to harm myself. To an extent, it has meant finding healthy alternatives, but at times it has meant feeling the need to harm, but not acting upon it.

It has been five years now since I 'gave up' self-harm and I consider myself to be recovered. Prior to that, I had experienced about four years of self-harm, approximately five or six times a week, although at times they would occur all on the same day. I was twenty-three when I started harming. Self-harm, to a certain extent, was a primal need and an addiction.

I really only realised what the true meaning of 'recovery' was; when a close friend spoke about someone he knew who was battling alcoholism. He said that the friend was 'easier to be around when he was drinking' and this puzzled me at first. When I questioned my friend about what he meant by that, he went on to explain that when an addict was battling with their addiction, the reality was that was all that they were thinking and talking about was the addiction, so to all intents and purposes, they were not recovered. This really struck a chord with me.

When I had stopped harming, I believed that I was 'recovered' but that state can only happen once the thoughts and urges to harm no-longer exist, when the plaster and bandage aisle in the supermarket no-longer cause my heart to quicken and when I stop longing for the feel of cold metal on my skin. So, in reality, I was not 'recovered' for quite some time. Recovery is a process which takes years, maybe even a lifetime.

- Is recovery about 'getting better' or learning to deal with self-harm as part of living?

Recovery is not about preoccupation of the mind on 'not self-harming', but about seeking the opportunity to live a life where self-harming is no longer a potential outcome in any situation. When starting to compile this piece of writing, I truly believed that I was recovered. I had not thought about harming myself in several

85

years and I had dealt with my anger, upset and frustration at general life events in a more healthy manner, or at least, in a more socially acceptable one!

Then, earlier this year, I was stopped by the Police for speeding and I quite suddenly had to battle those old demons – the urge to self-harm was back with a vengeance. Regardless of my explanation, speeding was wrong, but at the time it was unintentional. I was struggling to keep my head above water at work and I was driving home after being at my niece's first birthday party on a Sunday evening on the motorway, thinking about all of the work that I would need to do when I got in. My speed had crept up without my noticing until I saw the blue lights in my rear-view mirror.

By nature, I am a rule follower. I never break any rules that I am aware of because it allows me to go about my daily life carrying less stress and anxiety. When my speed was questioned, I was honest, took the fine and the three points on my previously perfect drivers' license and went home. For the first time, in a very long time, I felt as though my life was out of my control and I struggled to contain my anger at myself.

I felt the need to harm myself, to punish myself more than I already had been by the Police, so that I could feel back in control of the situation, and ultimately my life. The strength of those feelings were overpowering, so much so, that I was unable to cry, or sleep, or do much of the work that I needed to do for the next day. I didn't self-harm. That night felt as though I was keeping a sort of strange vigil for myself, ensuring that I would not give in to the urges and I got through the night, although the anger and frustration remained with me the next day. It wasn't until my shame became so overpowering that I felt the need to share the story with my sister that I found it easy to breathe again.

Her response was the complete opposite of what I thought I deserved. She simply laughed. She didn't laugh at me, but laughed at the story of how I had managed to overtake a Police car while speeding! I had been unable to see any humour in the situation before then, and I experienced an instantaneous feeling of relief. It went from a secret burden I had to carry, to becoming an amusing anecdote to share with friends and colleagues, and none of them seemed to think any less of me, which helped me to readjust my perception of myself.

Now, a few months later, I can see that I needed my recovery from self-harm to be tested at a time where those urges could not be predicted and to see that I could ride them out on my own, in order to know that I really had recovered from my addiction. I also needed to see that my old triggers didn't leap back to the forefront of my mind just because I had revisited old ground that it didn't mean 'back to square one.' The main motivation that particular night in not giving into my urges to harm, was the absolute knowledge that if I were to, it could be the start of a slippery slope and I could not stand the thought of leading myself back there.

When I had initially self-harmed, I had ended up there unintentionally, if I gave in now, it would have been an active decision to let the life that I had worked so hard for to unravel completely, and I couldn't be sure that I could make my way back to recovery again. I did not want this to be a life-long battle of lapses with limited success, I could forgive my initial bought of self-harming, but anything after that would be unacceptable to me. My black and white view of the world, at times, can be just the clarity that I need.

Looking back, there was a period of time where I felt as though life without self-harming was like 'living life without a safety net.' I haven't 'taken' to being alive too easily, in fact, I have always felt as though I have had to learn to be a social creature, where others seemed to take to it so naturally.

Self-harm was something I could use to exert my frustration at my social (and academic) failings and retain an illusion of social competence. In a way, I couldn't emotionally keep up with my acting skills, and the self-harm bridged the gap.

- What could professionals do more effectively to support/assist individuals?

I don't think that I can offer any groundbreaking advice to those professionals who find themselves working with (or against, as the case may be!) people who self-harm. It has all been said before, most of it is plain common sense. But, for those who wish to be reminded, or are interested in what worked for me in my recovery, I would say that being treated with respect would be the centre of all beneficial care.

Someone who harms will never stop so long as they see disgust or judgment in the eyes or tone of voice of the people who are meant to help care for them. Never suggest that self-harm is 'a cry for help' or 'attention seeking'- there are far less painful ways of doing both those things that will not physically scar you for life.

Realise that suicide and self-harm are not the same thing. Self-harm keeps those who are suffering alive, suicide does not. Consider the fact that self-harm exists in many, many forms, not all of them with visible evidence. Poor self-care and taking risks with personal safety are examples of self-harm too. I self-harmed on many levels, I expect that many other sufferers will too.

- What might help people be more aware regarding self-harm/injury?

I would like to think that the campaigns which encourage equality for people who are experiencing poor mental health are becoming more and more regular, and with such a positive presence on the Internet, self-harm, along with other symptoms of anxiety/depression will become easier to talk about. I do worry that having too much information available could cause the number of people choosing to harm, to increase.

My own self-harming came from an urge that I experienced, rather than from another's suggestion, but I have experienced how the ideas of others can be a trigger. A few years ago, I agreed to take part in a study into the methods used and frequency of people's self-harming. At the time I was in a 'good place' and was not triggered by the questions in the survey, but I did finish it with additional information that I had not considered before, for example, I had never thought of deliberately burning my skin, or trying to break bones. I didn't do either of those things, but I then had additional ideas that I had not previously had. Couple that information with a poor emotional state, and I could have acted upon those urges.

I think that everyone should be encouraged to be sensitive towards those who seem to be taking poor care of themselves generally, not specifically self-harm. Like I have said before, self-harm does not always translate as cutting, it could be a multitude of self-destructive behaviours.

- What does recovery from self-harm actually mean in real terms for an individual who has/or is self-harming?

In the last five years that I have been 'clean,' I have only self-harmed on one occasion. To some, that may seem as though I am not really recovered, but I believe that it proves the complete opposite is true. I was faced with the very sudden end to my marriage, a relationship with someone who I loved and had supported me emotionally for more than ten years, a situation which would be catastrophic to anyone. That event took place four years ago now and I did self-harm out of frustration and from the extreme emotional pain that I was experiencing at the time. There was nothing within my powers to change the situation and that feeling of powerlessness led to me acting on my urge to harm.

The proof that I have recovered from self-harm is that it has not happened again since. It was the one off that proved that the hold that self-harm used to have over me, was no longer there. Yes, there was temporary relief because I was focused on something other than my emotional pain for a few minutes, but afterwards I did not feel any of the benefits that I had enjoyed previously. I was entirely unimpressed; there was no calm, no thrill, nothing, other than feeling a bit silly.

For me, recovery has meant no longer having the need to self-harm in my life and for it to no longer 'work' for me. As more time passed, I faced up to stressful situations without hurting myself and as a result developed an attitude of 'self-care' instead.

Recovering from self-harm, where there are physical scars from emotional pain, leaves you with a sort of 'badge of honour' that only other ex-harmers can really appreciate. I have chosen not to hide my scars on my arms because I am not ashamed of them and feel that I could justify that period of my life to anyone who questioned it. I could confidently challenge any person to go through what I have gone through and come out of it unmarked, never mind as successfully as I have. This will probably surprise people as I am a teacher.

I am in a responsible role, at times, helping others to deal with their own emotional difficulties, educating children on emotional resilience. It may be even more surprising that I am a primary teacher. I think it is important to see that people who self-harm and who have recovered from self-harm come from all walks of life. It is not an affliction for any particular age group, gender or sexuality. Just like cancer and depression, self-harm is an equal opportunities employer where someone feels the need to feel as though they have a little control in their lives. Something, I would suggest people feel the need for more, and more these days.

When I see other people choosing to leave their scars in plain sight, I almost feel the urge to give them a hug or a 'high five' because we are unwittingly part of the same club. There is a comfort from knowing that others have felt and acted on those very same urges that I have experienced and that they think it is acceptable for the evidence to be in the public domain too. It is a silent encouragement to others.

It is an obvious conversation starter for someone who wants to know how they can kick the habit too. I am quite confident that if I was in a line-up with twenty or so other humans, no-one would pick me out as being someone who had self-harmed. Despite popular belief, there is no particular type.

Bruce Wallace

'Alex'

Getting better is easy right? Say you had a chest infection, sure it's painful, hurts like anything, but you go to the doctor, he gives you a pill and bang, may take a week but you get better. I wish self-harm was that easy to recover from, that there's a magic pill, it stops you, it cares for you, doesn't that sound nice?

If only it was true, I'm a student, in my final year at college, I've been a self-harmer for nearly 5 years. I've tried to recover 5 times, each time I've failed, but this time? This time is going to be different.

I've had support, sure I have counsellors and doctors, but I'm not someone who can be helped like that. I've had online counsellors too, they're fab while the session lasts, but they're not there during the urges, during those dark times at night. In terms of parents, well, my mother don't understand, my dad chooses to ignore it, the rest of my family haven't been told, my parents are ashamed of it. They think I will "grow out of it".

But why do I think this time is going to be different? Because this time I've found something to help, something to aid in the dark hours. Some people find dancing or singing, I found writing.

It's amazing, I can sit down with a bit of paper and a mind full of hurt and I can transform it into something beautiful. Funny thing is I'm Dyslexic, kids used to take the mick out of the way I used to spell and write, but now I'm well on my way to completing my first novel.

Recovery won't be easy, no one said it would be, but I believe strongly that it will be worth it. There is no magic pill for self-harm, nothing to take it away. You are the cure yourself, you decide to get better.

I believe we can live without self-harming, there is always a light at the end of the tunnel, it's there, getting closer every time we say no, it's there reminding us there is something beautiful at the end.

Recovery means getting better, means getting over something. And that's what I'm going to do. I never planned to hurt myself; it was like a fire deep inside which only blood could put out. Maybe that's how it starts, with fire.

Bruce Wallace

'Gemma'

I was diagnosed with depression when I was 15 and had been self-harming for a while but didn't tell anyone, including the doctor.

It was a very lonely time because I was so ashamed of myself for what I was doing and I made every effort to prevent anyone from finding out. I used to love sport and really enjoyed gym class but I'd make excuses like having stomach ache so I could sit it out and not have to bare my arms.

I didn't feel like I could talk to anyone. I was too ashamed to speak to my family and worried my friends would think I was just attention seeking. The 'emo' culture was a big part of that. Anyone who self-harmed was branded an emo and thought to be doing it for attention. But it certainly wasn't attention seeking, I was terrified of anyone finding out.

There were times when it felt like my whole world was caving in and I could see no future for myself. Unable to deal with my emotions, I would get so upset and engulfed in grief that harming myself seemed like the only thing to do. People can confuse self-harm with being suicidal but for me at least, it was the exact opposite. Self-harm was my only way of coping and of staying alive. It was like a pressure valve when everything got too much and a way of reminding myself that I was still alive when I got so down that I felt nothing at all.

Of course, those around me eventually did eventually find out. I was careless one night at home and left my arm outside a blanket I'd used to cover myself while watching television and my mum saw my arm. She asked what had happened and I said I'd fallen down some stairs outside my school. I knew she didn't believe me but she didn't ask any more questions.

The next day my sister and I were out walking and she got a text from my mum telling her to try and look at my arms. She asked why this was and seemed concerned. I didn't feel I had any choice so I showed her my arms. Her attitude immediately changed from concerned to angry. She shouted at me and asked why I was doing it. But one thing my sister said really stuck with me: "What's so bad about your life that you want to die?"

No matter how much I tried to explain that I didn't want to die and why I did it, she just didn't understand. The fact that she was angry with me for doing it only made feelings of guilt and worthlessness even worse. I don't hold a grudge about it, I know now that it was ignorance that led my sister to think and act that way.

Ignorance about self-harm from my sister and my mum I could accept, but from the medical profession I cannot. After being referred to the child and adolescent mental health services I saw a psychiatric nurse once a week. One week he noticed the scars on my arms and asked if I'd been self-harming. I took a big step by saying yes and letting him know, but he responded 'Well they aren't really deep cuts so that's fine.'

At the time I was young and still had those feelings of shame about my self-harm so neither of us ever said any more about it. It wasn't until a few years later when I was thinking about it that I realised how awful an attitude to self-harm that was. Especially for someone in that profession.

I got most of my help and advice around self-harm from the Internet. It was somewhere I could ask questions and look for advice without anyone judging me. Maybe I would have been able to stop using self-harm as a coping mechanism sooner if I had sought help but at the time I preferred to deal with it on my own. And it worked to an extent. It has been 3 years since I last self-harmed. Despite experiencing depression again in that time, I have managed to stay self-harm free.

When I think about it, I'm not sure I really have recovered. Although I no longer cut or burn myself, I'm not sure I am much better with dealing with my emotions. These days when I am very stressed or feeling low I tend to over eat. This is less of a problem than self-harm but what it says to me is that I never really learned how to deal with the emotions, which lead me to self-harm.

Chapter 5
RECOVERING THE BODY: SELF-INJURY, SCARRING AND
RECOVERY
Amy Chandler

Introduction

In terms of recovery, people who have self-injured, by
cutting or burning their skin, might face different challenges from
people who have taken overdoses. In this chapter, I discuss the
role of bodies in the accounts of twelve people who had self-
injured. I focus on the ways in which bodies might be implicated in
explanations for continuing to self-injure; and accounts of stopping
(or, perhaps, recovering from) self-injury. I also suggest that where
there is permanent scarring, the bodies of people who have self-
injured necessitate particular ways of accounting for recovery. How
scarred bodies are understood can vary significantly. In some
cases, self-injury scars might be viewed as positive marks of
healing, power and strength; in others, scars can be seen as
stigmatising marks of difference, madness or illness. In what
follows, I hope to highlight the importance of meaning and
interpretation, and perhaps offer some possibilities for optimistic or
affirmative readings of self-injury and scarring; whilst remaining
realistic about the constraints of wider social and cultural attitudes.

Between 2007 and 2008 I spoke to twelve people as part
of a doctoral research project exploring the life-stories of people
who had self-injured, from a sociological perspective (Chandler,
2010). Participants were recruited through a range of community
sites (online and offline), and through snowball sampling. Each
participant took part in two interviews with me. The first interview
focused upon their 'life story'; while the second addressed self-
injury more directly, discussing different experiences and
explanations they had for their own or others' self-injury. Interviews
were transcribed, and analysed using a combination of narrative
and thematic approaches.

Narrative approaches involve paying close attention to the
context in which interview data is generated, and in particular
looking at the way that stories are told by participants (Riessman,
1993). Examining interview data in this way can provide insights
into how meaning and understanding are constructed by
individuals; and how these meanings can be located within wider
socio-cultural contexts. A key focus of my analysis was the role of
'the body' in self-injury (Williams & Bendelow, 1998). Although
authors are now beginning to highlight the importance of this (Adler
& Adler, 2011; Inckle, 2007), when I began my research bodies

95

were strikingly absent from existing (academic) accounts of self-injury.

An important feature of the context in which this research project was carried out, and the interviews held, is my own identity as someone who has also self-injured. This feature was made clear to all participants at the start of their involvement in the study. While traditionally, researchers have attempted to maintain distance from participants, in order to maintain 'objectivity', such an approach has been strongly criticised as inappropriate, unethical and impractical (Finch, 1984; Stanley & Wise, 1993). As such, I felt it was more ethical, and would make my research practice more transparent to routinely disclose my own relationship to the topic of study. Participants were encouraged to ask me questions if they wanted, and the interviews proceeded in most cases in a spirit of mutual exploration and discussion.

The ways in which self-injury was talked about and explained varied widely between participants and indeed within individual accounts. In part, I would suggest that this variation led from the diverse life-experiences of the people who participated. The people I spoke to included five men and seven women, aged between 21 and 37 years old. Eight people described themselves as having 'stopped' self-injury, saying that the last time they had injured themselves was between one and eight years prior to their interview with me. The other four indicated that they continued to injure themselves, and in most cases reported doing so between their two interviews.

Participants had widely different experiences with self-injury: for some self-injury was something they had done (or continued to do) regularly; for others self-injury had occurred on only a few occasions. Some participants had been diagnosed with psychiatric illnesses, and received a range of treatment and support; others had never sought formal help for either their self-injury, or any other associated problem (such as substance use, or mental distress). Participants also had different explanations for their self-injury, although there were some commonalities. For most, self-injury was described as being, at least in part, about managing problematic emotional states (Chandler, 2012).

None of the participants in the research talked explicitly about recovery with regard to self-injury. However, exploring their accounts of their experiences of self-injury, whether on-going or in the past, provides useful insights into what recovery *might* mean to people who self-injure. In what follows I discuss three themes from the accounts of participants, which can be related to recovery. Firstly, I highlight the lack of explicit recovery narratives in these accounts, suggesting that this poses a particular problem to the idea of recovery *from* self-injury. Secondly, I discuss the accounts of those participants who continued to self-injure. Thirdly, I introduce the accounts of two participants who talked explicitly about self-injury as a *method* of recovery. Finally, in conclusion I point to the importance of bodies in accounts of self-injury, and explore the challenges faced by those who have permanent scarring from self-injury.

- Recovery by proxy: Moving away from self-injury

In most cases, the participants in this research who no longer self-injured did not frame this as something they had actively chosen to do. Rather, they talked of gradually finding different ways to cope; or of changes in their circumstances that removed an issue they had previously had to 'cope with'. For several participants, greatly reducing, or stopping, alcohol use was implicated as an important factor in their moving away from self-injury. Craig described injuring himself largely by cutting between the ages of around 17 and 20. His narrative suggested that self-injury was closely tied to drinking excessively, and he characterised both as damaging and irresponsible behaviours associated with being young:

> *I think it's because you, as I say with other things, you realise that you're not just harming yourself in a lot a respects, there's other people either directly you are harming just by being an idiot, or, people who are, you know, sort of upset by what you're doing because they don't wanna see you, harming yourself or whatever. Which took me a while to realise [...] Cos I think it's an important factor, I don't think it's easy to say that, "I only did it because I drunk".* (Craig)

As indicated in this quote, Craig suggested that over time, he became more aware of the impact his drinking and self-cutting might have on others; as well as noting the difficulty of admitting the potential link between self-injury and drinking. Craig was not alone in making this connection, and in the accounts of three other participants, self-injury and drinking were associated, and 'stopping' self-injury was clearly related to 'stopping' drinking.

Justin was one such example. His account described two discrete periods of his life where he had self-injured. The first occurred when he was aged around 16, and he attributed this largely to youthful experimentation along with general unease about life. He noted that he could not remember 'why' he stopped injuring himself at this time, but suggested he did not injure himself for several years. He self-injured again during a period in his early 20s when he was drinking excessively. Justin characterised his self-injury during this time as more 'angry' and related to feelings of self-hatred. His account indicated that both his self-injury and his drinking 'stopped' following a serious accident that had occurred when drinking and required hospital treatment:

> ... and then one, once I'd done that [the accidental injury], that seemed to sort of, you know, ... I went home, didn't drink, that much at all, em, ... and, you know since then never, [pause] never kinda contemplated it [self-injury] again. (Justin)

Other participants identified similar 'turning point' incidents, which, in hindsight, precipitated them 'stopping' self-injury. While in Justin's account this incident was an accident, for some participants the incident was an act of self-injury. The manner in which these incidents were narrated varied. For Milly a particular act of self-injury was framed as signalling the end of her engagement with self-injury:

> ... that was, that was my last [act of self-cutting], really ... it was the crux. [...] I said I think that's it, I've given myself a real scare, a really bad scare, [...] and I think there have only been twice since then, where the urge has taken me over [...] And, it always... well, no not always sometimes it comes and... really scares me sometimes, if I'm feeling down, or, worrying about someone, this idea'll pop into my head and it freaks me out. And my coping mechanisms now, are either to phone somebody, or to go on the computer and have a faf, cos I'll forget about it.

Milly's narrative framed self-injury as a way of coping with problematic emotional states. The excerpts above show how Milly suggests that although the 'urge' to self-injure occasionally returns, she now has alternative methods of coping. These new 'coping skills' were acquired over a long period of time, during which Milly also stopped drinking and described engaging in different forms of therapy, and changing parts of her life she was unhappy with. Her account suggested that she had largely stopped self-injury *before* these changes occurred.

That self-injury had represented a particular way of managing difficult emotions, which was gradually replaced by other emotional management techniques, was a common way in which participants described moving away from self-injury. These accounts were not framed in a way which indicated that any great effort had been put into 'stopping' self-injury. Rather, participants' accounts described making more general changes to their lives, partly as they 'grew up' or 'went through' difficult times, which accompanied their gradual cessation of self-injury.

> *I don't expect to do it again, it's sort of I guess it feels like it was a process that I, helped me to cope with things in my life at the time, that I sort of gone through that now [...] don't, don't really need that as a, as a coping strategy anymore* (Francis)

The context in which these changes occurred appeared to be more important than individual commitments to recovery from or cessation of self-injury. Limited longitudinal research with people who have self-injured suggests that the majority (though certainly not all) of people who injure themselves as adolescents report not doing so by the age of 30 (Moran et al., 2012). This suggests that with self-injury – as with drug use – 'natural' recovery occurs. The narratives discussed here indicate the importance of wider changes in individual lives, the kind of changes that might be expected to occur during late adolescence, and which may be implicated in a move away from self-injury.

- Not recovering?
  Explanations for continuing self-injury

In exploring what recovery might mean for people who self-injure, it is also important to consider what it might mean for people who continue to self-injure. The four people who took part in the research who continued to injure themselves talked in different ways about the prospect of stopping self-injury. Anna was 33 and had been cutting herself for five years; she talked in an ambivalent manner about her future use of self-injury. When I spoke with her she was engaged with a range of support services for on-going mental health problems; and some of these were aimed specifically at helping her to minimise the harm caused by her cutting. For Anna, recovery in terms of 'stopping' appeared to be a long way off:

> *If I'm having a really bad spell and I'm cutting myself a lot...if I can get past that, and get past like the first sorta few days then I dinnae consciously go 'oh yes, another day, yes another day' it's just a case of, its fine, its forgotten about ... d'you know what I mean I dinnae think about it and I dinnae focus on it and... hopefully that sortae carries it on longer... and it just takes that one trigger, to, to, to set you back... it's when you are doing it, are cutting yourself then it's a case of oh! I shouldnae be*

> *doing this, I have to stop, I have to break this cycle[1]*
> (Anna)

Anna's account here is complex. She refers to the difficulty of 'stopping', sometimes even for more than one day; however her account also suggests that when she does not cut for a while, this is something that 'just happens' rather than being something she actively strives for. In this way, Anna frames herself as not having control over her practice of self-injury: rather, she described it as a reaction to outside 'triggers'. This implies that any recovery in terms of stopping would have to come from a change in circumstances (an absence of 'triggers'), rather than (or perhaps as well as) an active engagement in choosing not to self-injure on Anna's part.

Other participants also referred to self-injury in terms of uncontrollable 'urges'; for instance, Harriet said "*sometimes, you just find, that the urge is so strong that you do it, without thinking*". Such language serves to position self-injury as something that an individual might not have control over. Recovery in this sense is less about overcoming an illness, and more akin to recovery in terms of overcoming an addiction (Victor et al., 2012). Indeed, the concept of recovery remains intensely important in terms of substance misuse and addiction; though its use has not gone without criticism (May, 2001; Pearce & Pickard, 2010).

The feelings that self-injury is used to manage or evoke, and the effects that self-injury can have are inherently embodied. The visceral, corporeal nature of cutting and burning the skin; and the effects that these acts can have were framed by participants as centrally important in explaining why self-injury might be a difficult practice to stop. In some cases, participants framed this in positive language, emphasising that in many cases self-injury was highly successful in enabling them to manage problematic emotional states.

> *I don't think I'll ever completely stop, it might, I might, could be able to go years without doing it or whatever, but I don't think, right that's it I'm done, I'm never going to do it again because I can't say that. And, you know sometimes you do need to think something different and that nothing*

---

[1] The research was carried out in Scotland, and the transcriptions have attempted to reflect as accurately as possible the way that participants talked. Dinnae = did not; shouldnae = should not; sortae = sort of, etc.

else [other than self-injury] will make you feel something different. (Belinda)

Belinda was aged 21 and had been cutting and hitting herself since she was 16. Belinda's account highlights two potential problems with the concept of recovery as applied to self-injury: a) the difficulty of finding an alternative that has the same, embodied, effect; b) the difficulty of saying 'never again'. Belinda described self-injury as something that she did relatively infrequently, in response to feelings of anxiety that became unbearable. She talked about self-injury as acting to stop her experiences of racing thoughts and rising anxiety – to help her 'feel something different'. Other participants also noted that self-injury could be difficult to replicate; some mentioning 'distraction' techniques such as drawing on skin with red pen, snapping elastic bands around one's wrist, or holding ice cubes. In most cases these were said to be ineffective:

I think it's, it's really difficult to get somebody to, sort of, use alternatives, because it's such a powerful, em, thing and because it involves the body so strongly and, ... but its, you know like the, ... the actual cutting and the, the blood thing and, there's not much else that can kind of, stand in for that really. (Rease)

I did the ice... tried that a few times cos, ken when you grip like... ice in the ... [...] It's no... it's just... disnae have the same effect... and it must be like... It must be like a druggie getting their fix, and I can only assume but [pause]. Something does happen, when you cut yourself. (Anna)

Understanding what self-injury can do for those who practice the behaviour should be central to exploring what recovery might mean. Anna was clear that her view about her on-going self-injury could be seen as 'defeatist', she was not hopeful about the future, or about her ability to 'recover' from either her practice of self-injury, or her wider struggles with her mental health. However, Anna's story was not entirely bleak; she *was* surviving and – arguably – her self-injury was an important aspect of *how* she was surviving (Warner & Spandler, 2011).

- Self-injury as recovery

In some cases, participants who had stopped injuring themselves positioned self-injury as transformative, a practice that had played a key role in their 'recovery'. These accounts were intensely positive interpretations of what self-injury could do, and the embodied effects it had. Rease, for example, was the only participant to talk explicitly about 'recovery' from mental health problems. She described her self-injury as making her feel better; the cuts and burns generated ultimately *good* feelings, which enabled her to cope with depression and anger.

> [*Self-injury*] *was a really positive thing, it really made me feel better [pause]. And, as long as I can remember I had this rage inside me, I still have it, em, but I'm able, more to deal with it now, [before I was] constantly filled with rage, and don't have an outlet for it, and doing that [self-injury] just made me feel so much better. It kinda moved onto razor blades as well. [and] I was filled with joy! It's one of the best things that ever happened to me! Just wonderful. It just really made me feel alive again, and that I could cope, and, also I was very, em, kind of prone to suicidal thoughts, and, self-harm was, kind of a way, ... to deal with that, and kinda, keep myself alive. I mean I've always said, if I hadn't have self-harm I wouldn't be here, I'd be dead. Em, and I don't say that lightly, I mean that's really true.* (Rease)

Rease's narrative positioned self-injury as the beginning of a long journey, whereby she began to feel more comfortable with her body, more in control of her life. Self-injury was framed as an important part of this process. Rease also alludes here to the idea that self-injury helped her to avoid acting out her suicidal thoughts. Ultimately, Rease began to explore other means of managing her feelings of anger, and her narrative strongly emphasised the importance of being creative, listening to music, writing, and doing art as ways of channelling strong feelings. This was echoed in the narratives of other participants, who similarly talked about finding different ways to manage their emotions, which enabled them to 'need' self-injury less and less.

Mark's narrative of stopping self-injury also emphasised the positive effects of the practice. He was clear that although his self-injury occurred at a time where he had been struggling with depression; self-injury itself had represented a positive act in the face of inertia. Mark described in detail the last time that he had cut himself, an act which he framed as being in response to an extremely difficult interpersonal situation. During a heated discussion, Mark cut himself in front of a person he had an intensely problematic relationship with. He suggested that the effect of this was that:

I calmed down instantly, and, actually [unclear] em, … and it worked, it worked, again, em, I think that's what I said in the email, it's [self-injury] always had a positive, feeling to me. (Mark)

The act of self-injury in this case 'worked' in that it ended a tense conversation and also ended the problematic relationship. The injury left a visible scar, which Mark talked about in ambivalent tones. On one hand, the visibility of the scar felt uncomfortable, as it indicated the injury had been 'worse' than intended; simultaneously, the visibility of the scar was interpreted by Mark as a reason not to cut again:

But, because that one was so bad, em, … it almost serves as, as a [...] I don't need to cut, I've got that. [...] It's like er, it's like a badge. think if I hadn't done that, my arm would have been a lot more – covered in small cuts (Mark)

Rease and Mark's accounts were distinct in framing self-injury as an important part of resolving difficult feelings, including depression and anger. Each emphasised the successful nature of self-injury, which echoed the accounts of those participants who continued to use self-injury. In contrast, Mark and Rease indicated that they had not injured themselves for some time, but nevertheless provided optimistic and affirmative accounts of their previous practice of self-injury.

- Bodies and scars: accounting for recovery

I suppose and like, sort of mental distress you're going through which, maybe in a few years or, a couple of days or months or something kind of, changes and kinda, transforms or maybe even dissipates, em, you've still got those scars, you know, of what that meant and, where you were at. (Rease)

I've stopped cutting [...] but they're still there, they are very much in the present tense [...] I'm someone who has cut, and that is a present tense [...] I am someone who has cut, it's not that, I used to cut, its, it's definitely still [...] I guess it's just a kind of reminder. (Mark)

The presence of permanent scarring, as suggested by the excerpts above from Mark and Rease's interviews, pose a challenge for those who have 'stopped' self-injuring. Participants related a range of strategies through which they managed the assumptions of 'other people' regarding their scars. This included: lying about the origin of scar, being 'honest', covering scars with tattoos, clothing or jewellery, using scar minimisation techniques (e.g. creams or oils designed to reduce appearance of scars). However, what I would like to emphasise here is that the presence of scars might influence the type of accounts that are possible regarding self-injury, and the prospect of recovery. Elsewhere I have suggested that people who have self-injured (as opposed to those who have self-poisoned) have to *account for* their scars regularly (Chandler, 2010; Chandler, 2012). These scars are an irrefutable part of their body – and bodies are often seen as representative of identities (Budgeon, 2003). Participant's narratives about their scars suggested that there were various ways in which scarring could be incorporated into coherent, if not always particularly positive, self-narratives.

For some, including Rease and Mark, scars were described positively, as marks of something that had been endured and overcome. This did not mean that participants were always comfortable revealing scars, but it did suggest a possible way in which scarring could be explained in a satisfactory but not overly self-deprecating manner. In contrast, other participants' narratives indicated more discomfort with the presence of scarring. Notably, Anna, Belinda and Robert who all described continuing to injure themselves at the time of the research, talked about their scars much more negatively. Anna, for instance suggested that her scars provided a reason *not* to stop self-injuring:

> *I've got these scars now, they're there now, the damage is done, I just cut on top eh scars now, just, covered... totally utterly covered [pause] so it's like [...] what's the point, of stopping?* (Anna)

Similarly, Robert talked about his scars as reminders of difficult or upsetting times. Emma, who had not injured herself for several years, said that while she did not regret making the scars, she did regret and struggle with managing their existence. In particular, she did not feel able to reveal them to her parents, who she suggested would be "horrified" by them. Indeed, most participants, even those with relatively positive interpretations of their scars, recounted difficult social situations where scars were questioned or remarked upon. It was difficult, if not impossible, for some participants to entirely 'move away from' their earlier use of self-injury; it remained with them in a visible, embodied manner.

- Concluding thoughts

One of the key problems with some uses of the notion of recovery, is that it can serve to locate the 'problem' securely within an individual whilst at the same time framing that individual as potentially 'out of control' (Pearce & Pickard, 2010). The individualisation of much discourse on recovery can result in a minimisation of the problems leading up to or surrounding self-injury (or addiction, or mental ill-health), factors which may be outside of the individual (Harper & Speed, 2012). This does not mean individuals are powerless or entirely without agency; but it does highlight the need for careful and nuanced assessment, and an acknowledgement that self-injury does not arise solely out of an individual's 'pathology' nor necessarily solely out of a 'pathological' environment. Rather, self-injury needs to be understood as a complex manifestation of problems both within and without the individual who is cutting or burning their skin.

Bruce Wallace

References:

Adler P., and Adler P. (2011), The Tender Cut: Inside the Hidden World of Self-Injury, New York, New York University Press.

Budgeon S. (2003), 'Identity as an Embodied Event', Body and Society, 9, 1, pp.33-55.

Chandler A. (2010), 'Pain Incarnate: A narrative exploration of self-injury and embodiment (unpublished thesis)', Edinburgh, University of Edinburgh.

Chandler A. (2012), 'Self-injury as embodied emotion-work: Managing rationality, emotions and bodies, Sociology, 46, 3, pp.442-457.

Finch J. (1984), "It's Great to Have Someone to Talk to': Ethics and Politics of Interviewing Women', in Bell C., and Roberts H., (Eds.), Social Researching: Politics, Problems and Practice, London, Routledge.

Harper D., and Speed E. (2012), 'Uncovering Recovery: The Resistible Rise of Recovery and Resilience', Studies in Social Justice, 6, 1, pp.9-25.

Inckle K. (2007), Writing on the Body? Thinking Through Gendered Embodiment and Marked Flesh, Cambridge, Cambridge Scholar's Press.

May C. (2001) 'Pathology, Identity and the Social Construction of Alcohol Dependence', Sociology, 35, 2, pp.385-401.

Moran P., Coffey C., Romaniuk H., Olsson C., Borschmann R., Carlin J.B., and Patton G.C. (2012), 'The natural history of self-harm from adolescence to young adulthood: a population-based cohort study', The Lancet, 379, 9812, pp.236-243.

Pearce S., and Pickard H. (2010), 'Finding the will to recover: philosophical perspectives on agency and the sick role', Journal of Medical Ethics, 36, 12, pp.831-833.

Reissman C. (1993), Narrative Analysis, London, Sage.

Stanley L., and Wise S. (1993), Breaking Out Again: Feminist Ontology and Epistemology, London, Routledge.

Victor S.E., Glenn C.R., and Klonsky E.D. (2012), 'Is non-suicidal self-injury an "addiction"? A comparison of craving in substance use and non-suicidal self-injury', Psychiatry Research, 197, 1-2, pp.73-77.

Warner S., and Spandler H. (2011), 'New Strategies for Practice-Based Evidence: A Focus on Self-Harm', Qualitative Research in Psychology, 9, 1, pp.13-26.

Williams S., and Bendelow G. (1998), The Lived Body: Sociological Themes, Embodied Issues, London, Routledge.

'Rachel'

A lot has happened in my life. When I was young, roughly the age of two I was abused by my babysitter. When I was six I was abused again by my dad's girlfriend's son and throughout my whole life my family do nothing but put me down and don't accept me for who I am.

At the age of twelve I was constantly arguing with my mum. I felt so much anger for her! I started to self-harm. Cutting was what I did, it was my release. I ended up running away from my mum and her partner; I didn't want to be round them. I finally went home with a little help from my friend and had an hour's conversation with the police who examined my arms and wanted me to go to hospital but I refused.

The self-harm carried on and I went to a counselling service known as CAMHS, which is child adolescent mental health service. I went once for an assessment and was told I would be ok...a month later I was back due to running away from home. This time I stayed with them. In February 2009 I couldn't take life anymore and took an overdose and ended up in hospital for four days till I was deemed ok to leave. The constant arguing with my mum didn't end. My self-harm decreased slightly but it was always there in my head. If I saw a knife a thought in my head screamed do it just do it....

Self-harm is something you live with, from the moment you make the first cut to the moment you die. It's a sad truth but a truth none the less. I am now eighteen and again going through another difficult patch and self-harm is once again playing its part. The urge to do it is stronger than ever and I have tried three antidepressants in the last six months. My friends often ask how I am but I always hide the truth. Self-harm will never leave me. The scars I have because of them remind me of the struggles I have come through and I know this probably sounds strange but it helps...to see the scars and know you got through some difficult times. I can't explain the thoughts.

Recovery seems a long way off and even though people will say that it will stop my self-harm...it won't because self-harm is a part of me now and always will be.

My heart goes out to all those who are going through self-harm.

Think before you make the first cut...

Bruce Wallace

Chapter 6

SELF-HARM AS AN EVOLUTIONARY RESPONSE TO EMOTIONAL DISTRESS
Maria Naranjo and Lora Coyle

In order to explore the relationship between self-harm and recovery, we first need to identify what self-harm is and how people "discover" it. There is a great debate regarding how people first come in contact with self-harm.

In this chapter we are going to present the notion that self-harm is a natural primeval response to psychological distress. In order to elaborate on this theory we will enrol help from evolutionary psychology and anthropology. We will explore the similarities and differences between organic self-harm, self-injurious behaviours and self-harm.

At present, it is estimated that 80,000 children In the United Kingdom present signs of severe depression, some as young as five (Green, McGinnity, Meltzer et al, 2005). One in ten children and young people aged 5 – 16 years suffer from a diagnosable mental health disorder - that is around three children in every class. Between 1 in every 12 and 1 in 15 children and young people deliberately self-harm (YOUNGMINDS). If self-harm is a natural response to psychological distress, that may explain its epidemic dimensions in western society. We know that there are factors that precipitate the engagement in self-harming behaviours, which include personal, societal, environmental and life experiences.

Research (Larkin et al, 2014) highlights the fact that people whose family or friends use self-harming behaviours are more likely to engage in self-harm themselves. The act of self-harm tends to be kept secret. However, in some settings such as family homes or psychiatric in-patient hospitals, people may observe self-harm. In turn, the person may copy the behaviour and start hurting him or herself as a consequence of observational learning.

The question remains that not everybody starts self-harming as a consequence of observational learning. Hence, why do people engage in self-harm the first time? Where do they get the idea from? It seems to me a counterintuitive idea, i.e.: *if you are hurting psychologically or emotionally, inflicting physical pain on your body will make you feel better.*

> *"I was thirteen at the time. I felt so alone and confused. I couldn't understand the thoughts going through my head. It was like I had so many thoughts going through my head*

that I didn't know what I was thinking about. And I just was playing with a paperclip. I had opened it all up and I scratched myself, it felt good so I continued to scratch myself" (Lora Coyle, Hurting to heal, 2013)

Lora explains that she was playing with a paperclip and scratched herself by accident. According to Chandler (2012) there is some evidence pointing to the fact that some people "find" self-harm when exploring with objects such as compasses, paperclips and suchlike.

Most people are unable either to recall or to articulate the process by means of which they started self-harming. Some people, however, are very clear that they found it by "accident". Griesbach (2008) carried out a qualitative study and one of the findings suggested that a proportion of people came across self-harm by accident. In some cases, people were upset and they hurt themselves by chance, then realizing that it felt better. In other cases, the intention was ending their lives; however they survived the attempt and discovered a coping mechanism that made them feel better.

Could it have been a helpful behaviour before our ancestors developed language?

For the purpose of this chapter we will talk about self-harm as an umbrella term that describes a continuum of harmful behaviours that range from socially acceptable nail biting at one end to self-mutilation at the other. Self-injury is defined as any damage inflicted to body tissues, such as cutting or burning.

Self-injurious behaviour is another term for self-injury normally applied to refer to the stereotypical behaviours that people with learning disabilities and/or animals may engage in.

There are mainly three theoretical frameworks to explain self-injury, these include self-injury within an addictions paradigm, operant conditioning and observed learning.

In this chapter we are using the addictions paradigm. According to this theoretical framework, the brain releases beta-endorphins when people self-injure. This mechanism is part of human natural response to stress and physical pain. People who self-injure normally experience a calm and relaxed mental and physical state after the act. This is a consequence of the endocrine processes taking place in the body. It is possible that people become physiologically and psychologically habituated to this mental state. Furthermore, addiction to endogenous opiates is well documented. Van der Kolk, Pierre and Herman (1991) concluded that phenomena such as dissociation, self-destructive behaviour and impulsivity are hormonally mediated behaviours elicited in response to earlier trauma or abandonment.

Furthermore, recent research using brain imagining has discovered that the opiate system is triggered not only in response to physical pain but also in response to social rejection.

> "*In general, opioids have been known to be released during social distress and isolation in animals, but where this occurs in the human brain has not been shown until now.*" (Nauert, 2013)

It has been accepted for some time that the opiate system is involved in both the reduction of pain and promoting pleasure. This study suggests that it extends to emotional pain experienced in response to social rejection.

As we have mentioned earlier self-injury is not unique to humans, self-injurious behaviours in animals are well documented. Many animals kept in isolation, neglect and in cages use self-injury to cope with the situation. Hence, it seems that being reared in isolation in zoos or laboratories are predisposing factors. It is important to highlight that parenting and rearing conditions do not predict self-injury in primates. The common denominator seems to be social isolation. These behaviours are often seen alongside emotional arousing stimuli, such as responses to anxiety and stress. And now it makes sense, they are being stimulated by a release of opiates in the bloodstream in response to their social environment.

Social grooming is a social strategy for many animals, including humans, to establish dominance, resolve conflicts, build coalitions and aid social collaboration. Social grooming releases beta-endorphins. That is one of the reasons why the effects of grooming are relaxing. Hence, it would seem that the same opiate system is activated in response to grooming and social rejection.

The concept Self-Directed Behaviour is a combination of behaviours that include self-scratching, self-grooming, self-touching in primates. Its primary function seems to be assessing relationship security.

Sometimes highly sociable animals (including humans) are in situations where social contact is dramatically reduced and they lack the control to change their state such as being kept in isolation, either real or perceived. These situations could trigger an over-grooming response.

Opportunities for human interaction and positive physical contact are in decline in our society. As discussed in a previous chapter the increase in the usage of new communication technologies, is changing the human social, emotional and psychological landscape at an unprecedented speed with unknown consequences.

Human bodies are designed to cope with bouts of stress. Increasingly our bodies are being subjected to prolonged periods of exposure to stressors in the environment. It may be possible that our bodies equipped with an ancient programming to survive are developing alternative natural ways to combat stress, and self-injury is one of them.

In summary, it would appear that self-injury could be a behaviour that bypasses our cognitive capacity and relies on our primeval brain to reduce the effects provoked by long term exposure to stressors. Furthermore, this behaviour may become physiologically and psychologically addictive due to the intervention of hormonally mediated responses to stress.

The relation between neurological development and trauma in early childhood is starting to become clearer. There is growing evidence from brain imaging research highlighting functional and structural effects of trauma and exposure to stressors in childhood.

More research is needed in this area to prevent people from resorting to self-injuring in the first place. Furthermore, more work needs to be done to ensure children and young people have the best start in life.

References:

Castlesa Duncan L., White A., Aurelie F. (1999), Social anxiety, relationships and self-directed behaviour among wild female olive baboons. Animal Behaviour Volume 58, Issue 6. December 1999, pp.1207–1215

Chandler A. (2012), A Self-injury as Embodied Emotion Work: Managing Rationality, Emotions and Bodies, Sociology, June 2012 46: pp442-457

Favazza A. (1998), The coming of age of self-mutilation, Journal of Nervous and Mental Disease, 185(5), pp.259–268.

Green H., McGinnity A., Meltzer H., et al., (2005), Mental health of children and young people in Great Britain 2004, London: Palgrave

Griesbach D. (2007), An in-depth qualitative exploration of the links between self-harm and attempted suicide in young people, Scottish Government

Jones I.H., and Barraclough B.M. (2007), Auto-mutilation in animals and its relevance to self-injury in man, Acta Psychiatrica Scandinavica, 58 (1), pp.40–47

Larkin C., Di Blasi Z., and Arensman E. (2014), Risk Factors for Repetition of Self-Harm: A Systematic Review of Prospective Hospital-Based Studies, DOI: 10.1371/journal.pone 0084282, accessed 31st May 2014

Mental Health Foundation. (2006), Truth hurts: report of the National Inquiry into self-harm among young people, London, Mental Health Foundation

Nauert R. (2013), Brain Eases the Pain of Social Rejection, Psych Central, Retrieved on November 7, 2013.

Turner V.J. (2002), Secret Scars,

Van der Kolk B.A., Perry J.C., and Herman J.L. (1991), Childhood origins of self- destructive behavior. American Journal of Psychiatry, 148, pp.1665-1671,

YOUNGMINDS. Mental Health Statistics, available at http://www.youngminds.org.uk/training_services/policy/mental_heal th_statistics, accessed January 2014

Bruce Wallace

'Sarah'

Hi, my name is Sarah and I am someone who is in recovery from self-injury. I say in recovery rather than recovered because thoughts of self-injury are never far from my mind, and I don't know if I'll never slip and cut again, it's such an old coping mechanism for me. But for now, each day I choose not to cut.

I don't actually remember the first time I self-injured deliberately. I just know that by age 10 it was an established pattern. How did I start? Probably by accidentally burning myself and discovering that physical pain could make emotional pain go away. At any rate I was hooked.

Throughout my childhood and teenage years I self-injured regularly, alternating between burning, cutting, and scratching the skin off my arms until I bled. Remarkably nobody noticed or if they noticed nobody said anything, because I never made any attempt to hide my injuries. It didn't occur to me to be ashamed of them it was just something I did.

My mother died when I was 13, and my Dad followed that up by getting and staying drunk for 2 years until he started attending grief counselling, promptly met a woman and married her within 6 months. She wanted a husband not a precocious teenager so she made it clear I wasn't welcome in her house, so I spent a lot of time alone in the basement or walking the streets of Ottawa. It made self-injury easy, because nobody was paying attention.

Remarkably I stopped self-injury in my late teens on my own volition when I figured out that my best chance of getting out of the house was a scholarship to a university – preferably one very far away from Ottawa. So I channelled all my emotions into studying and extracurricular activities so that I'd have a good application package, and I lost the need to self-injure. Mission accomplished, I got the scholarship and left home entering into what was the happiest time of my life.

In my 20's self-injury wasn't anywhere in the picture – I was too busy with school, with extracurricular activities to build my resume, and then building a career. Along the way I went back to school part time to get my MBA. But I still wasn't dealing with my emotions in a healthy way. You see at the time, I was also starting to develop a drinking problem. I was the classic work hard, party hard, workaholic, alcoholic. No time for feelings.

That stopped working in my late 20's and on the advice of friends, who were tired of me bursting into tears every day at lunch, I started therapy. Plus I was having problems at work, and I figured if I said I was getting outside help they'd be less likely to fire me. Therapy was intense and brought up all kinds of stuff but was helping until a notable Christmas in 2001 when I was 32 years old. My therapist and I were talking about my Mother's death that was difficult for me, and then after an intense session, she informed me that she was going on vacation for 3 weeks. Talk about sideswiped – old grief, plus old abandonment issues equalled emotional crisis, and I remembered something that always worked.   Cutting.   So one evening, I literally plied apart one of my razors, pulled out a razor blade and started cutting geometric patterns into my arm.   I was instantly filled with calm, and the raging emotions, which I describe as a black tide receded.   I'd found my solution which became the start of a decade long dance with self-injury.

I remember at the time, being very ambivalent about self-injury. I sensed it wasn't normal, I didn't know anyone else who did it, but it worked for me so I wasn't ashamed of it, once again it was just something I did.

When I first told my therapist I was cutting, I was lucky. As a trauma specialist she had lots of experience working with women who self-injured.   So she didn't judge me, try to force me to stop, or in any way make me feel bad about it; she just explained it as a coping mechanism.   At my next session she handed me a stack of articles about self-injury and wound care, all downloaded from the Secret Shame website, run by Deb Martinson.   It was like a light bulb going off, other people did this, there was a name for it, and most importantly there was an on-line support site, Bodies Under Siege or BUS for short.   Suddenly there were all these other people who did what I did, got my emotions, and understood that cutting worked.

I continued to cut actively for a period of about 3 years, again not making much attempt to hide it.   Interestingly again nobody really noticed or at least pretended not to and nobody commented on it – I think they were afraid to ask.   But all the time I was on BUS gradually learning to express my emotions and slowly trying to stop cutting.   I was, with the support of people on BUS and my therapist, eventually able to stop with periodic slips with long periods of non-self-harm in between.

Since 2007 I've pretty much been self-injury free, except for maybe 3 slips when things got bad enough that I felt I needed to cut.   The last time I cut was in January 2012, and I regret it, because it's the first time after all those years of self-harming, that I was left with visible scars on my arm.   I don't know, maybe that's my sign that it's time to stop for good.

I've subsequently been through a program of dialectical behavioural therapy, and that helped me a lot to learn to regulate my moods without resorting to self-destructive behaviours. Unfortunately in Canada, DBT is horribly underfunded and programs are hard to find. I was lucky enough to find and be able to afford a private program.

I continue to be involved with BUS. I've been on staff at the site since 2005, and am currently one of seven volunteer systems administrators who keep the site running. Partly it's my way of giving back to the community that helped me so much, and partly because it keeps the sadness and desperation I felt around cutting fresh in my mind, so that I know very clearly that I don't want to go back there. It's also been a great support site for me in my attempts to stop drinking.

Whenever I get intensely emotionally upset today, my first instinct is always to reach for a razor blade. Sometimes I trace the scars on my arm and think it would take the pain away in 30 seconds. But I also remember how I'd feel the next morning, sad that I hadn't coped better, that I'd given in, and embarrassed that I'd have to go back to BUS and tell them I'd slipped and cut. So I don't cut. I also really hope that I've stopped for good this time, because I really don't want to be the little old lady sneaking blades into the senior's residence. And I also feel that I deserve to not hurt myself. So each day I make the decision not to cut. And every day I don't cut, I feel like I've accomplished something.

I have now also stopped drinking, which really was just another form of self-destruction for me, and I view both my drinking and my cutting similarly. They're both lousy coping mechanisms that offer fast, immediate short-term relief in exchange for some pretty serious long-term pain. I'll probably always have thoughts of both, particularly in times of crisis. The difference is today I have a choice. I choose not to drink and I choose not to self-injure. I've learned new ways of coping that I choose to use instead.

In a perfect world, I'd wish that I didn't still have thoughts of self-harming and that I could say with 100% certainty that I'm never going to cut again. And maybe that day will come. But for now it's enough for me to not act on my impulses, and that's my recovery – making better choices.

Bruce Wallace

Chapter 7
THE ROLE OF THE INTERNET IN RELATION TO SELF-HARM AND RECOVERY: FRIEND OR FOE?
Bruce Wallace

Having previously explored the links that may exist between self-harm and recovery this chapter will now attempt to identify the role that the Internet may play in this context. Within the modern world many people now take for granted access to and use of this medium as a means of acquiring, confirming or utilizing information in a myriad of situations; e.g. social, educational, economical, financial. Health related information is now readily available from both reputable and possibly less reputable sources, identifying one of the issues that often raises concerns regarding the credibility of information. As a vast repository of information the Internet poses a number of challenges when attempting to identify specific information that is of good quality and may be of benefit to individuals.

In the case of self-harm there is now a significant amount of information readily accessible. A brief search undertaken by the author to demonstrate how many 'bits' of information may be identified in an area such as self-harm is clarified in the table at the beginning of the following page. The terms self-harm and self-injury were entered using five of the most popular search engines and the following responses were identified:

Date search undertaken: 8th July 2014:
Search terms: Self-harm
                          Self-injury

Search 'Engine'	*Search Term*	*Number of 'hits'*
GOOGLE	Self-harm	63,300,000
	Self-injury	15,300,000
AOL	Self-harm	17,200,000
	Self-injury	15,400,000
MYWEBSEARCH	Self-harm	15,900,000
	Self-injury	25,900,000
BING	Self-harm	4,150,000
	Self-injury	1,100,000
YAHOO	Self-harm	4,160,000
	Self-injury	1,100,000

The examples offered in the table above identify the number of results obtained by just using the one term, whilst acknowledging the existence of a number of different terms (e.g. others could include *self-injury; non-suicidal self-injury; non-suicidal self-harm; deliberate self-harm; intentional self-harm*) that could have additionally been searched for. Many other search engines exist but tend to provide lists that exclude a numerical indicator of the number of 'hits' on the list. The availability of so much information of variable quantity and quality introduces a dilemma familiar to many mental health practitioners identified in the question below;

Should use of the Internet as a source of support for people who self-harm be supported or opposed?

The question posed on the previous page draws a range of responses with many professional publications now acknowledging that the Internet is an indispensable part of modern life, especially amongst young people. Bell (2014) provides an interesting addition to the debate by suggesting that more prominent posting of information should be undertaken by 'professional mental health organisations' to improve the reliability of information that individuals may be able to access. The challenge faced by those seeking information (e.g. individuals who are self-harming) and those who provide it (e.g. health/social care professionals) is highlighted in a survey carried out in 2012 contained in the 'Talking Self-Harm' (no date) report. Here the ways in which young people most frequently seek out information related to self-harm is identified statistically as:

•	Talking to friends	45%
•	TV or Radio	29%
•	Social Media (e.g. Facebook, Twitter)	25%
•	Newspapers/Magazines	24%
•	Information provide by school	24%
•	Talking to a teacher	19%
•	Websites that discuss it	19%
•	Talking to family	19%
•	Charities	17%
•	Talking to health professionals	11%

(p27)

Irrespective of the many opinions that are apparent throughout the published literature exploring this topic, it might be of value to look at how information tends to be 'presented' on the Internet. This, in part, will be determined by who is creating the information and who it is primarily intended for. Information regarding self-harm and the Internet tends to exist in two domains, namely:

Literature – this takes many forms including books, booklets, leaflets, poetry and articles (e.g. research, academic, experiential) and explores the relationship between the Internet and self-harm and its impact on the individual. Although the quality of information may vary the final product due to the process involved in compiling and publishing tends to result in some degree of control.

Internet sites. These again consist of a number of formats. They include:

- Those whose exclusive focus is around the topic of self-harm (e.g. LifeSigns; Selfharm; Nshn) and who have frequently evolved into a resource-based facility that provides information, advice, training and/or support related to self-harm.

- Those that include information on the topic as part of a much wider information base (e.g. Royal College of Psychiatrists; MIND)

- 'Training' sites – here information is available that enables individuals to access a range of materials intended to address deficits in knowledge or to support greater awareness of signs that may indicate the need for professional assessment and intervention. One such site recently launched (March 2014) is MindEd that is supported by a group of organisations and has as its focus the mental health of children and young people. There is information related to self-harm available on this site.

- BLOGS – here individuals have generally created their own site and the information is frequently a personal journey/diary of experiences related to self-harm. It may also be individuals who have studied and/or researched the topic and use this type of forum as part of the dissemination process. Sometimes the information is collated on other sites (e.g. time-to-change.org.uk; self-injury.net) with a number of blogs included.

- Social Networking sites – e.g. Facebook, Tumblr, Bebo, Myspace, Twitter and Google+. These are just a few of the multitude of sites currently available. They range from sites that may be perceived as 'general' to others that have a specific focus on an area, for example music or films. With some of the sites individuals and groups may overlap as many organisations have a presence via links within their main sites, particularly via Facebook (e.g. LifeSigns; The Royal College of Psychiatrists).

The difficulty faced by 'social' sites is based on their popularity and the difficulty faced in policing the range of information posted and interactions that take place. An example demonstrating this difficulty is based on a brief search carried out by the author during the writing of this chapter. A relatively straightforward and brief search yielded access to a site that had pictures and video clips of self-harming behaviour many of which were quite graphic in their demonstration of injury. There were also clips linked to weight loss and poetry exploring suicide. A "trigger" warning was noted but only after entering the page.

A wide range of advisory material is available offering guidance on safety but this is primarily aimed at children and young people (e.g. Childnet International, UK Council for Child Internet safety, Stonewall Education Guides) with less noted for older people who may be less familiar with the risks associated with 'surfing' the Internet.

An area not mentioned in the relationship to information available is that provided in visual form, i.e. pictures, video. This is an extremely powerful media and has the potential to be quite destructive when encountered by vulnerable individuals. Areas online such as YouTube provide a range of visual material related to self-harm but frequently in the form of advisory/supportive clips. The difficulty that is faced by anyone looking for appropriate advice and support is complicated by the sheer number available (173,000 on YouTube alone; search dated 18th April 2014).

Online groups:
Online groups will frequently on their main page outline what they perceive their role to be. Some information may be seen as clarifying what might be available in terms of resources and/or support as illustrated by the examples offered below:

'We consider ourselves to be one of the good guys – we try to keep things as safe as possible while letting you express what's happening for you in the way you need to' (selfharm.co.uk)

'it's our continuing mission to guide people who hurt themselves towards new ways of coping, when they're ready for the journey' (lifesigns.org.uk)

'Empower and enable individuals that self-harm to seek further support and alternatives to self-harm' (nshn.co.uk)

'The WISH centre is a charity supporting recovery from self-harm, violence, abuse and neglect' (thewishcentre.org.uk)

'Bristol Crisis Service for Women (BCSW) is a national organization that supports girls and women in emotional distress. We particularly help women who harm themselves, often called self-injury' (selfinjurysupport.org.uk)

'Harmless is a user led organization that provides a range of services about self-harm including support, information, training and consultancy to people who self-harm, their friends and families and professionals' (harmless.org.uk)

The above examples offer a brief overview of what is available (a more detailed and extensive list is provided in the resources chapter). What is apparent is the amount of information that is available in a variety of media formats (e.g. written, video, pictures, PowerPoint) but what is most challenging is attempting to determine what may be of help and what may not. Individuals looking for information and support or advice have a vast wealth of information to call upon but may have difficulty in determining between that which may be of help or may not. In addition some material may actually be detrimental to the individual's welfare and not all potentially distressing or shocking material (especially visual) will have a "triggering" warning displayed in advance. This is clarified in the example given in a paragraph on the previous page linked to the author's search for information using the Internet.

Health (including mental health) literature:

Mental health practitioners appear to be somewhat ambivalent regarding the Internet and what value it may offer, particularly when it comes to self-harm and recovery. There is now an emerging acknowledgement of the importance of modern technology in relation to how people communicate and some concerns regarding how such a vast repository of information can be effectively 'policed'. It is also seen by some as an immediate form of communicating and information sharing, introducing additional challenges. Occasional difficulties have arisen where people have made comments on social networks or blogs and these have been deemed libellous culminating in the individual appearing in court and being fined. Although this is rare it identifies one of the many challenges faced by people actively using the Internet as a communication medium.

It is against this background that mental health practice struggles to establish an effective presence that will be seen and utilized by those who may require help, advice, support, and/or information. The following is a reflection of some of the emerging research, together with some historical publications to offer a contextual comparison on how this medium is viewed.

Dejong (2012) looking at the professional relationship and issues such as boundaries, confidentiality and consent introduces some interesting comments regarding the additional challenges faced by professionals who use the Internet to communicate with their clients. In table 1 in the article, information included:

- A 2010 survey of Executive Directors at US state medical boards found that 92% had received reports of online professional violations
- A 2011 survey of practicing physicians found 34.5% had received a "friend" request from patients or their family members

NCSBN (2011) in their guidance on use of social media by nurses cautions individuals to be aware that it can be difficult to ensure that personal and professional boundaries are maintained within the virtual environment of the Internet. The white paper provides a number of advisory points including the following:

'Maintain professional boundaries in the use of electronic media. Like in-person relationships, the nurse has the obligation to establish, communicate and enforce professional boundaries with patients in the online environment. Use caution when having online social contact with patients or former patients. Online contact with patients or former patients blurs the distinction between a professional and personal relationship. The fact that a patient may initiate contact with the nurse does not permit the nurse to engage in a personal relationship with the patient'.

It might be pertinent at this point to note that there is a growing use of the Internet for both seeking and sharing health related information. Chretien and Kind (2013) stated in their article that a 2011 survey identified that: '*23% of US adult Internet users with chronic medical conditions had gone online to find others with the same medical conditions*'.

Swannell et al (2010) indicate that due to the fact that individuals they may be working with might have been utilizing the Internet for advice and support then it might be pertinent for professionals to recommend 'quality internet sites to their clients'. An interesting alternative is offered by Boyd et al (2011) who finish an article on challenges posed by the Internet by stating:
'*The Internet has made it easier to find and share problematic content, but it has also made it easier to find at-risk youth and share healthy messages. Developing new strategies that leverage the opportunities afforded by the Internet are going to be more effective than any form of legal regulation*'. (p32)

Daine et al (2103) in their review of literature on the subject of the Internet and its influence concluded that it had potentially both a positive and negative influence. The positive influence was perceived as:
'*the internet is also used as a support network and a coping mechanism, and can connect people who are socially isolated*'.

The ambivalence regarding the Internet and the role it can play is continued in the article by Harris and Roberts (2013) who conclude:
'*There are clear and important benefits to engaging in website use for many individuals, however, these are not experienced by all website users*'.

Tatum and Hubard (2009) in their book continue the discussion about both positive and negative issues by identifying a range of positives in Internet use (e.g. reduction in physical barriers, degree of anonymity, moderation) together with less positive attributes (e.g. lack of moderation, control/reliability of information, lack of visual cues).
Whitlock et al (2006) indicated some interesting points in their study including:
'*What the self-injurious adolescents in our study appeared to do online is what most people who trust each other do in conversation: exchange support, share personal stories about daily life events, and voice opinions and ideas*'.

'the Internet plays a powerful role in shaping opportunities for adaptive and maladaptive social interaction'.

Sharkey et al (2012) in their interesting study on 'protective talk' indicate that individuals may find online support both helpful and challenging.

Powell (2011) ironically in an online commentary article responding to a published paper considers it important to undertake research to:

' investigate the relationship between self-harm community use and actual behaviours, including the effects on health and social outcomes'

Prasad and Owens (2001) in one of the older articles looking at the role of the Internet take a slightly different approach and acknowledge the importance of the Internet as a source of information through a search using key terms and a 'meta' search engine. They identified that one of the issues that should be considered is:

'We concluded that professionals involved with people who self-harm would benefit from knowing something about the kind of material available to those who visit websites'.

Baker and Fortune (2008) follow a similar theme some seven years later and in their abstract state:

'If health professionals and researchers hope to understand people who use self-harm and suicide websites, and engage them in their services, they must take a more balanced view and not focus solely on the possible risks associated with using such sites'.

This theme is seen quite frequently in published material and another piece of research (TheSite.org, 2009) that comments both on professionals and individuals accessing information via the Internet states:

'Access to care and support was seen as difficult due to the lack of understanding from health professionals. Good services were described in terms of being readily available, with staff who had a non-judgmental attitude and a high level of knowledge regarding self-harm.

'Websites were mentioned as a valuable source of information as long as they are run professionally and are relevant to the need of the young person'. (p4)

Lewis et al (2014) in a recently published article indicate that in research undertaken utilizing Google to establish what information was available when a focused search was undertaken:
'Nonsuicidal self-injury-related search terms are frequently sought out worldwide and are likely to yield noncredible and low-quality information that may propogate common NSSI myths'.

When considering the statement above regarding the reliability of information that may be available Halgin and Whitbourne (2009) introduce an interesting thought on maybe why the Internet attracts such attention from young people, particularly individuals who self-harm:
'In light of the significant role that emotional inexpressivity plays in self-injurious behavior, it is not surprising to find a proliferation of internet websites in which young people are calling out anonymously in the hope of communicating their pain and discussing their experiences'. (p451)

It may be pertinent to finish this section by introducing a reference cited in a thesis by Sellerberg (2012). It does not answer the original question posed by the title of this chapter but introduces another variable to consider when determining perceptions regarding the Internet and its usage:
'In research on how young people interact online to discuss sensitive topics, interviews with individuals who practice self-harm disclose the fact that it is the invisibility of the body in online interaction that allows them to talk more openly and freely (Johansson, 2010:148-55)'.

Summary:

Part of the difficulty faced by both individuals who may be self-harming and those who wish to help is the ongoing ambivalence encountered when discussing the value that may exist in the use of modern technology, specifically access to the Internet. There is a proliferation of information now readily available but not all of it is necessarily reliable or valid. Different sites provide varying degrees of information for differing reasons and for differing audiences. Literature published on the topic acknowledges that there are potentially both positives and negatives associated with utilizing the Internet. The greatest concern expressed is around how people may respond if their search encounters information that may be both inaccurate and in some cases potentially constitute a risk to the individual's welfare.
It is noted that a number of interventions are now available from a mental health perspective in such areas as

Cognitive Behaviour Therapy via the Internet and recent sites such as **Beacon** (available at beacon.anu.edu.au) allow access to a greater range of resources and information. Ybarra and Eaton (2005) indicated in their article that information could even be considered an intervention. Another innovation that is gathering momentum is the use of 'apps' to aid the therapeutic interactions between practitioners and service users in mental health. An example of one such idea is that of '*Buddy*' where the author indicates:

'*Buddy is a digital tool that is helping to strengthen links between therapists and clients by providing a simple way for users to share their daily thoughts in the periods between appointments*'. (Penfold, 2012)

Although not specifically utilized with individuals who self-harm, the ideas reflected in the article could be considered as a way of helping to improve the communication between an individual seeking help and the ongoing supportive infrastructure needed for this to be effective.

The question of whether recovery associated with self-harm may be facilitated in part through access to and use of the Internet remains unclear. It may be a matter of individual choice regarding what the Internet means, what value (if any) it introduces to the situation and what the person is actually looking for. A recent concern has been raised over the fact that some young people may use this medium to berate themselves in what Boyd in her Blog calls 'digital self-harm'. The individual may set up multiple accounts in order to pose questions (their account) and then respond in a negative or quite destructive manner (using another account with different username). Boyd (2010) indicates this may be due to a number of reasons and indicates these might be seen as:

- It's a cry for help
- They want to look cool
- They're trying to trigger compliments

(Boyd, 2010)

This again provides conflicting information in as much as at least one of the elements appears to asking (albeit in a convoluted way) specifically for help whilst others convey the distress that the individual is experiencing, again albeit it in a way that only tends to become clear retrospectively.

An initiative that is being launched in the state of Victoria in Australia will involve teachers and school staff receiving training in mental health issues and self-harm. The Schools and Families

Engaging Minds program will include online training with videos as part of this process. Preiss (2014) explaining the initiative states:

'*The website that hosts the training program said early intervention would help tackle "emerging" mental health problems before they became more serious*'.

Whatever the dichotomy of views, opinions, concerns and reservations that access to and use of the Internet may pose, it is important to recognize that it is a significant consideration in decision-making. In areas such as accessing information, support, access to services, contact with others, interventions and recognition for self it is seen by some as an essential attribute in modern life. The many challenges regarding issues such as moderation, valid/reliable information, and whether major health/social and educational organisations should become more actively engaged in influencing the quality and quantity of specific information available will not abate. It may be fair to say that whether we like the idea or not the Internet is an integral part, potentially, of both the question and the answer!

References:

Baker D., and Fortune S. (2008), Understanding self-harm and suicide websites: a qualitative interview study of young adult website users, Crisis, 29(3), pp.118-122

Beacon, available at https://beacon.anu.edu.au

Bell J. (2014), Harmful or helpful? The role of the internet in self-harming and suicidal behaviour in young people, Mental Health Review Journal, Vol. 19, Iss: 1, pp.61-71

Boyd D. (2010), Digital Self-Harm and Other Acts of Self-Harassment, available at: http://www.zephoria.org/thoughts/archives/2010/12/07/digital-self-harm-and-other-acts-of-self-harassment.html (accessed 10th May 2014)

Boyd D., Leavitt A., and Ryan J. (2011), Pro-Self-Harm and the Visibility of Youth-Generated Problematic Material, 1/S: A Journal of Law and Policy for the Information Society, Vol. 7, pp.1-32

Cello, YoungMinds. (no date), Talking Self-harm, London

Chretien K.C., and Kind T. (2013), Social Media and Clinical Care Ethical, Professional, and Social Implications, American Heart Association, available at http://circ.ahajournals.org/content/127/13/1413 (accessed 12th July 2014)

Daine K., Hawton K., Singaravelu V., Stewart A., Simkin S. et al, (2013), The Power of the Web: A Systematic Review of Studies of the Influence of the Internet on Self-Harm and Suicide in Young People, PLOS ONE, 8(10):e77555, doi:10.1371/journal.pone.0077555

Dejong S.M. (2012), Networking, Professionalism, and the Internet, Psychiatric Times, available at http://www.psychiatrictimes.com/career/networking-professionalism-and-internet

Halgin R.P., and Whitbourne S.K. (2009), Abnormal Psychology, Clinical Perspectives on Psychological Disorders, London, McGraw-Hill

Harris I.M., and Roberts L.M. (2013), Exploring the use and Effects of Deliberate Self-Harm Websites: An Internet Based Study, Journal of Medical Internet Research, 15(12):e285

Johansson A., 2010, cited in Sellerberg J. (2012), To Transform the Body Online: Productions of subjectivity between the body and practices of written text in an online message board forum for self-harm support, Masters Thesis, Stockholm University

Lewis S.P., Mahdy J.C., Michal N.J., and Arbuthnott A.E. (2014), The State of Health Information Obtained Through Online Searches for Self-Injury, JAMA Pediatrics, Published online March 24, 2014. doi:10.1001/jamapediatrics.2014.187

LifeSigns, www.LifeSigns.org.uk

MindEd, www.minded.org.uk

NCSBN. (2013), White Paper: A Nurse's Guide to the Use of Social Media, Chicago, available at https://www.ncsbn.org/Social_Media.pdf (accessed 12th July 2014)

Nshn (National Self Harm Network), www.nshn.co.uk

Penfold J. (2012), Buddying up, Mental Health Today, Jan/Feb, www.mentalhealthtoday.co.uk/buddying_up_25769812925.aspx (accessed 8th July 2014)

Powell J. (2011), Young people, self-harm and internet forums, The Psychiatrist, pp.364-368

Prasad V., and Owens D. (2001), Using the internet as a source of self-help for people who self-harm, Psychiatric Bulletin, 25, pp.222-225

Preiss B. (2014), Schools get training for mental health intervention, brisbanetimes.com.au, accessed 3rd June 2014

Selfharm.co.uk, www.selfharm.co.uk

Sharkey S., Smithson J., Hewis E., Jones R., Emmens T., Ford T., and Owens C. (2012), Supportive interchange and face-work as 'protective talk' in an online self-harm support forum, Communication and Medicine, Vol9, No1

Swannell S., Oam, G.M., Krysinska K., Kay T., Olsson K., and Win A. (2010), Cutting on-line: Self-injury and the internet, Advances in Mental Health, Vol. 9, Iss: 2, pp.177-189

TheSite.org/self-harm. (2009), Self-Harm: Recovery, Advice and Support, Exploratory and evaluative research

Whitlock J.L., Powers J.L., and Eckenrode J. (2006), The Virtual Cutting Edge: The Internet and Adolescent Self-Injury, Developmental Psychology, Vol. 42, No. 3

Ybarra M.L., and Eaton W.M. (2005), Internet-Based Mental Health Interventions, Mental Health Services Research, Vol. 7, Issue 2, pp.75-87

'Nicki'

I started self-harming at the age of sixteen. I started for a number of reasons. I was confused about my sexuality, stressed with school and work and trying to be a sixteen year-old girl. I was struggling with everyday stressors as any sixteen-year-old does. When a friend had mentioned to me that he scratched himself when he was stressed, which helped him. I thought about trying it one day after being really upset and feeling really angry. Even to this day, I do not know what caused me to be so upset and stuff but I noticed a broche. Before I knew it, I was scratching myself and that is how it started.

It went on for about a year after that and then I did it less and gradually stopped completely after leaving school at the age of seventeen years old. I managed to stop for a whole year to year and a half. At the age of nineteen my mood started to drop. I became very depressed and started self-harming again. This time round I do not know how or why. Since then my self-harming became so bad that at one point I was cutting up to 5-10 times a day I think, especially at work.

From the age of nineteen, my life seems to have spiralled downwards as I have had a number of suicide attempts. My self-harm seemed a safe way to get out all those horrible feelings without hurting anyone else in the process. Even though I had seen the pain in my ex-partner's face at the time. I saw every time she noticed a new scar, but at the time I felt I had no control over my self-harm. I felt it was a way to punish myself for my feelings; it was also a release of my feelings at the time too. And there was the feeling of needing to, having no control over it.

Now I am four years into recovery I can even explain it like an addiction for me. I felt at one point I would never be able to live without self-harm. I have a safety box that my support worker at home helped me put together. She helped me figure out what to put in it to help me manage my self-harm urges. She also helped me to visualise a safe place, which helps me to stay calm and feel safe when stressed. My recovery has been going on for four years so far and I still have a long way to go. I think for me I will be spending a life trying to not self-harm, I believe it will become easier not to but the thoughts of self-harming may always be there; it is how I manage them now.

I have been in this hospital since June 2012 and already I feel I am managing differently. I last self-harmed in May this year. I believe recovery is possible because if you want something hard enough and you work with the right support you can make the changes and handle life without self-harm. I believe there will be hiccups, times where I may use a self-harming behaviour.

My self-harming was never intent to kill myself; it felt like a way of keeping me from suicide. I believe that I will recover with the new skills I am learning here at the hospital. I have had to come down to England, as there was no space in Scotland for someone with my diagnosis, borderline personality disorder. I am receiving Dialectal Behaviour Therapy, which I think should be available as much as Cognitive Behaviour Therapy because where CBT does not always help DBT might.

I believe that recovery is possible for everyone who self-harms with the right support and that starts with challenging the stigma that its only attention seeking youths that do it. I believe without my team of G.P., psychologist, psychiatrist and support workers I would never have made it this far in my recovery, never mind the team I am working with down here and then when I go home. I have been fortunate that I have not really come across a lot of stigma for my self-harm.

The hardest thing I have had to manage after the self-harm its self is the effect it has on my family and friends. I have had blinkers on, so to speak, for years thinking if I hide it no one will know, I went for a college interview for a care course and the tutor who interviewed me somehow knew I self-harmed and my scars were covered up. He did used to work as a mental health nurse before becoming a tutor at college.

I still to this day have no idea how he knew, which I think will puzzle me. The good thing was the tutors and the other students were brilliant with me.

Chapter 8
RESOURCES
Bruce Wallace

The information contained within this chapter has been collated to provide the reader with a range of material and/or links related to the topic of self-harm and/or recovery. It is not meant to reflect a definitive list or one that necessarily contains the most appropriate information for everyone. This is preceded by a list of links to information available on precautions that should be followed when using the Internet. These are intended to assist individuals on what might be called safe practice when accessing this medium. The amount of information available is quite considerable but always apparent. The author was aware of some guidance material but was surprised after a relatively short search to discover how much guidance is actually available and from a very diverse range of sources.

It is important to note that all of the links provided in this chapter have been accessed and explored over a period of time and were available at the time of checking. Due to the nature of the Internet links can change or be removed so it is important to save material that may be of interest at the time of discovery. A number of options may be available including:

- Downloading material to your computer
- Saving the link to your favorites or bookmarking (depending on system) [remember that this will be ineffective if the link no longer exists]
- Cutting and pasting information into a Word document and saving (remember to ensure that copyright is not being compromised here)
- There may be contact information provided by the site being accessed (e.g. email; phone number) offering you the option of contacting to enquire if information you are interested is available in other formats; e.g. booklet/leaflet/document/DVD

The most important thing to remember here is that information provided via the Internet may be transient in nature and there is no guarantee that it will remain accessible and/or available for any length of time.

The following section commences with a precautionary note regarding use of the Internet. This is not meant to sound negative but intended to draw the reader's attention to the 'rules' that should be adhered to, to ensure that the experience proves to be an interesting and potentially positive one and avoids some of the possible pitfalls that may be experienced otherwise.

Internet:

This medium is a vast repository of information and therein the problem arises. A quick search by the author (i.e. Via Google on 4th February 2014) using just the term self-harm revealed no less than 67,400,000 results in 0.22 seconds! This does not take into consideration other terms (e.g. self-injury, non-suicidal self-harm) that could also be searched for and also excludes any search related to the concept of recovery! Searching such a vast resource for information requires both an awareness of the need to be precise in search terms (i.e. 'key' words; phrases) and to ensure that you remember to save information when it is first accessed for later retrieval and viewing if required. Failure to do this may result in the frustration of being unable to locate a specific piece of information due to removing your history list from the browser ('tidying' your computer) or the sheer amount of information that you have looked through over a given period of time. As someone who has 'surfed' the Internet for information, initially without too much idea of bookmarking/saving a source for later perusal, the frustration of trying (in vain!) to locate it later is palpable.

Another very important element of Internet access and utilization is that of safety (regarding information value) when accessing this medium. Not all information that is encountered is accurate. If individuals search for specific information regarding self-harm it could result in inaccurate advice or conflicting information that provides little help or clarity for the person seeking it. It is important to remember that not all material posted on the Internet is carefully screened for accuracy and on some sites posted information may be accessed directly by individuals potentially altering content.

Additionally safety applies to the user. This is an issue that has attracted considerable attention as some of the information that people may encounter during their search may not necessarily be what they intended to find. This is currently attracting much debate around young people and how easily less desirable material and information may be readily accessible without some safeguards being put in place. The use of key words and/or phrases by an individual may not always result in information that they expected due to the actual search terms used.

Sharing of information is another way in which the Internet is utilized but individuals need to consider carefully some of the issues that are involved. Social network sites are now very popular with a very large number of Internet users. The opportunity to engage with groups and communicate with a diverse range of individuals brings with it some inherent issues that need to be considered very carefully by an individual when thinking about this process as something they might engage in:

- Are you ready to share information and allow other people to become aware of issues in your life that may up until this moment remained known only to you?

- Are you prepared for responses that may not always be positive?

- Are you aware that some of the communication may also take place anonymously without you knowing anything about the other person?

- Are you taking precautions to ensure that your personal details are protected to ensure your own anonymity as appropriate?

- Are you adequately prepared to enable you to use the Internet in a way that will support you whilst ensuring that the rules regarding safety, responding to others, profiles, and etiquette are respected and applied?

As a response to the points made above I have identified a number of resources that provide guidance for those using the Internet and again stress that this list is not exhaustive and offers some of the myriad of useful information that can be accessed and considered prior to becoming involved in issues related to self-harm and discussing and/or exploring these online. I have also included a range of links and some booklets that reflect the range of information that is available.

It is important to ensure that any information you access should be cross- referenced; something many students studying will be all too familiar with! A single source may or may not be a reliable information base but if you access several sources and they all provide similar information then this is more likely to reflect a more valid basis for the information. Obviously the sources should differ to ensure a broader basis for your search and if possible a sample of both formally recognized (e.g. NHS, education, police) and others (e.g. voluntary, social) will be more likely to generate this information.

The range of guidance, resources, booklets, information that follows is just a small sample of the vast repository of available material that exists and is offered purely to demonstrate what can be located with relative ease and may offer individuals a starting point.

Guidance:
http://www.thinkuknow.co.uk/
[Child Exploitation and Online Protection Centre]

http://www.thinkyouknow.co.uk/parents
Child Exploitation and Online Protection Centre (CEOP) [GB]

http://www.digizen.org/
[Digizen.org – Information on 'Digital Citizenship']

http://teenadvice.about.com/library/weekly/aa082802a.htm
[About.com – internet safety tips]

http://www.wisekids.org.uk/online_safety_tips_kids.htm
[Wise Kids – Online safety tips]

http://www.netsmartz.org/RealLifeStories/TeenPSA
[National Center for Missing & Exploited Children – NetSmartz Workshop]

 http://www.saferinternet.at/uploads/tx_simaterials/Facebook-Check_English.pdf
[Facebook – Checklist]

http://www.bbc.co.uk/webwise/accredited-courses/level-one/keeping-safe-online
[BBC – Webwise online course > Keeping safe online]

http://www.bullying.co.uk/cyberbullying/how-to-stay-safe-online/
BullyingUK – '*We provide a 24 hour helpline, advice website, email service, live chat and parenting/relationship support groups*'.

https://www.google.co.uk/intl/en/safetycenter/everyone/start/
[Google – Safety Centre]

http://safe.met.police.uk/internet_safety/get_the_facts.html
[Metropolitan Police Service – Safe]

http://www.nidirect.gov.uk/staying-safe-online

nidirect (Northern Ireland government services) - *'It's important to know how to stay safe when you're using the internet.*

www.internetmatters.org
[Newly launched site (May 2014) indicating that it is an 'independent, not-for-profit organization to help parents keep their children safe online'.]

www.fbi.gov/stats-services/publications/parent-guide
U.S. Department of Justice: Federal Bureau of Investigation – A Parent's Guide to Internet Safety

www.isafe.org
About i-SAFE – *'i-SAFE Inc. is the leader in Internet safety education'*.

Links:
http://www.lifesigns.org.uk/
LifeSigns – (Self-Injury Guidance & Network Support). The site itself outlines the organization as: *'an online, user-led voluntary organization, founded in 2002 to create understanding about self-injury and provide information and support to people of all ages affected by self-injury'*. A wide range of information and material is available within the various sections of the site.

http://www.nshn.co.uk/
National Self-Harm Network (NSHN) – Based in Nottingham the site information states that: *'NSHN was originally established to build a network of support groups for individuals who self-harm…The charity now focuses on support and distraction enabling people to seek alternatives to self-harm'*. A wide range of information and material is again available from this site.

http://www.harmless.org.uk/
Harmless – Based in Nottingham this organization indicates clearly on its home page that: *'it is a user-led organization that provides a range of services about self-harm including support, information, training and consultancy to people who self-harm, their friends and families and professionals'*.

http://www.penumbra.org.uk/
Penumbra – This Edinburgh based project encompasses a range of areas that are supported in the context of mental health but also has an area related to self-harm that indicates on its site that it was established to: *' provide a non-judgemental, friendly and user-led*

support service to people who self-harm'. It also mentions that 'the principles of hope and recovery are the foundation of our way of working'.

http://www.youngminds.org.uk/
YoungMinds – the site has a focus around young people and their emotional wellbeing and mental health. A section of the site has a focus related to self-harm and offers information primarily to parents. There is also a publication section and leaflet available aimed at young people who are worried about self-harm.

http://selfharm.co.uk/
[www.self-harm.co.uk] – Originated from a support organization based in Luton that had a focus on young people. The organization has expanded and now though its online resources provides: 'a safe online space available to inform and support young people who self-harm, as well as cater for the needs of their siblings, parents and friends. We also wanted to provide information and training for professionals like youth workers, teachers and social workers'.

http://www.basementproject.co.uk/
the basement project – The project has a contact address in Abergavenny in Wales and the site states that the project: 'provides support groups for those who have been abused as children and people who self-harm'. Information is available and a range of publications are identified on the site

http://www.selfinjurysupport.org.uk/
Bristol Crisis Service for Women (BCSW) – the site is identified with the title Self-injury support. BCSW is identified as: 'a national organization that supports girls and women in emotional distress. We particularly help women who harm themselves, often called self-injury'. A range of information is available and training workshops are also planned and delivered.

www.otbds.org/selfharmresources
Outside The Box Development Support – a Scottish based group who offer a range of training, material and support on the subject of self-harm.

www.mindswell.org.uk
Formerly HarmLess Psychotherapy – the site provides a range of information and training opportunities indicating: 'our aim is to reduce the need for people to resort to self-harming behaviours

such as drug and alcohol abuse, eating problems, self-medication, self-injury and other such behaviours'.

http://www.brighter-futures.org.uk/mental_health/scheme/echo
brighter futures : ECHO – this is a Staffordshire based resource that states on its site: *'provides mutual support for people who have experienced self-harm'.* The site indicates that training for professionals can be facilitated and for people who self-harm the opportunity to:

- Talk through with other group members in a safe environment
- Talk one-to-one with people who understand what you are going through
- Attend workshops to learn about new ways to cope
- Get information about other places that can support you
- Use the ECH helpline in times of crisis

http://www.thewishcentre.org.uk/
[The WISH Centre] – This centre is based in London and identifies that a range of resources, including training is facilitated. The site states that: ' *The WISH Centre is a charity supporting recovery from self-harm, violence, abuse and neglect'.*

http://www.childline.org.uk/
ChildLine – This site contains a page that has information relating to self-harm. It indicates that: *'This page contains information on why, how and who self-harms, how to tell somebody and getting help'.*

www.thesite.org
TheSite – This site has a section looking at issues related to self-harm where it indicates that: *'Self-harming is a personal thing and opening up to people can be scary, but it may be that you feel you want to talk about self-harm and the problems you are having. TheSite.org looks at how you can do this'.*

http://www.nspcc.org.uk/
NSPCC – This site has a section on: *'Helping children who self-harm'* with information and advice for parents, together with links for further help and information provided. There is also a specific area on the site
http://www.nspcc.org.uk/Inform/research/briefings/self-harm_wda101501.html that offers: *'Practice resources and research on self-harm'.*

141

http://mindingyourhead.info/topics/self-harm
Minding your Head info – Site organized and based in Northern Ireland with a focus on emotional wellbeing and mental health. It has some information on self-harm but offers links to a range of organisations and groups that provide specific information, support and advice.

www.rethink.org
Rethink Mental Illness – A site with a broad range of information related to mental illness. There is also a fact sheet offering information about self-harm. At 14 pages long it is quite detailed and provides a range of links to both organisations and material at the end.

http://ie.reachout.com/
Reach Out. com - A comprehensive site that states it: '*is a service dedicated to taking the mystery out of mental health*'. There is a section on self-harm that provides information and another that is an: '*ask the expert*' service that has included self-harm as one of the topic areas with the opportunity for individuals to: '*ask your questions and address your concerns*'.

http://www.yourmentalhealth.ie/
This site was developed by the HSE National Office for Suicide prevention and contains information about mental health, together with a section about self-harm. The information is brief but of value although it the page itself may be off putting as it is entitled: '*Self Harm & Suicide'*.

http://www.recoveryourlife.com/
Recover Your Life.Com – A self-harm community that states on its page: '*Although we are known for helping people suffering with Self-Harm, we also welcome and support people with other issues such as Eating Disorders, Mental Health problems, those dealing with abuse, and many more! We do not condone any pro-activity or encourage anyone to hurt themselves in any way*'.

http://www.nhs.uk/conditions/Self-injury/Pages/Introduction.aspx
[NHS Choices: Self-harm] – Information regarding self-harm, together with a list of useful organisations for further information]

www.national.slam.nhs.uk
[South London and Maudsley NHS Foundation Trust] – There is information regarding the self-harm service offered and it states:

'*Our service is for people who repeatedly self-harm and who have chronic interpersonal difficulties*'.

http://www.rcpsych.ac.uk/
[Royal College of Psychiatrists] – website contains a section on self-harm where information, leaflets and further information (via links) can be accessed.
Entering 'self-harm' in the search box at the top of the page (right hand side) returns a large range of material for the subject, including a collection of reports.

http://www.scottishrecovery.net
[Scottish Recovery Network] – organization with a specific focus on Recovery. A section on the website includes stories and a number of these have been submitted by people who have self-harmed.

http://www.sane.org/
Sane Australia – A comprehensive site that provides a range of information and resources on mental illness. There is a section on self-harm providing a factsheet and links if needing help, counselling or advice

http://au.reachout.com/
Reach Out. Com – This is the Australian site of reach out and provides both information and links for individuals who need information, advice, access to services.

http://www.headspace.org.nz/
Headspace – This New Zealand site is colourful in design and starts by stating that: '*everybody needs to find some headspace when life gets stressful and we hope we can help*'. There is a page on self-harming that provides information and links to additional sources of information.

http://sioutreach.org/
SiOS (Self-injury Outreach & Support) – This Canadian site is a collaborative venture between the University of Guelph in Ontario and McGill University in Quebec. It states: '*Whether you currently self-injure, have recovered, or know someone who self-injures and want to help, this is the place for you*'. A range of resources, including online videos, information and people's recovery stories are available.

http://www.selfinjury.bctr.cornell.edu/
Cornell University (The Cornell Research Program on Self-Injury and Recovery) – This American site was originally launched in 2003 and has accumulated information via research studies by the University resulting in material that is now being translated into: 'user friendly materials for individuals who injure as well as those who live with, care about, and work with them'. The site again contains an array of information arranged in an easily accessible way for a range of prospective users.

www.healthyplace.com
HEALTHYPLACE – This American site offers a range of material and information with a focus on mental health. It refers to itself as 'the largest consumer mental health site' and provides a section on self-injury.

Booklets:
All of the following booklets should be available by following the link provided. They provide the reader with some idea of the wealth of information that is currently available for a range of individuals and groups in different countries. Differences exist but it is also noted that many contain similar advice, guidance and information albeit expressed in a slightly different way.

http://www.nice.org.uk/nicemedia/live/10946/29425/29425.pdf
NICE (CG16) – The National Institute for Health and Clinical Excellence (NICE) has produced a booklet that is intended for: 'people who self-harm, their advocates and carers, and the public' and contains information that explains what should happen if and when someone presents to a health service resource and what good practice should occur. Practice guidelines have been issued to staff specifically related to people who self-harm.

http://www.mind.org.uk/information-support/types-of-mental-health-problems/self-harm/
MIND – Booklet providing information about self-harm. Available either to read on the site or can be downloaded as a twenty-four page PDF file.

http://www.barnardos.org.uk/about_self_harm_publications_tracked.pdf
Barnardo's/Mind (2007) – A twenty-three page booklet that provides a range of information on the subject of self-harm together with a couple of pages where further information can be obtained (from different organisations).

http://www.sane.org.uk/uploads/self-harm.pdf
SANE – Self-harm: The 'secret self'. This information sheet (15 pages) provides a range of information based on the results of research carried out with the involvement of 946 participants.

http://www.student.counselling.co.uk/Resources/Self-harm-Service-Booklet.pdf
South London and Maudsley NHS Foundation Trust (2010) – Booklet looking at what services may be available for individuals who repeatedly self-harm. A different perspective offered here as it looks at the service on offer.

http://www.ntw.nhs.uk/pic/leaflets/Self%20Harm%20LP%202013.pdf
Northumberland Tyne and Wear NHS Foundation Trust (2013) – Entitled: 'Self-Harm: A self help guide' this leaflet is actually more of a booklet (fourteen pages) and contains a range of valuable information. The site http://www.ntw.nhs.uk/pic/selfhelp/ also contains a large number of leaflets on a range of topic areas. Clicking on the self-harm leaflet will provide not only the booklet but also an introductory video linked to the booklet.

http://www.youngminds.org.uk/assets/0000/7354/Self-Harm_Single_page_.pdf
YoungMinds – A booklet entitled: 'Worried about self-harm?' this resource is aimed principally at young people who either self-harm or might know someone who does. It provides straightforward (but clear and valuable) information and a list of useful addresses and contact numbers towards the end.

http://www.mentalhealth.org.uk/publications/truth-self-harm/
A booklet written by Celia Richardson (2012). The information in based on the findings of the National Inquiry into Self-harm. It provides information in clearly identified sections and is a Camelot/Mental Health Foundation publication

https://www.google.co.uk/#q=booklet+on+self-harm+north+bristol+NHS+Trust
Bristol and Gloucester CAMHS (2011) 'Self Harm: Information and suggestions for school staff' – this booklet is quite detailed and over the twenty pages of content provides information, advice and further links for staff to follow up as required for additional information.

http://www.decd.sa.gov.au/speced2/files/pages/chess/hsp/Informati
on/revised_selfharm_finalweb.pdf

Self-Harm Booklet (Queensland, Australia) – interesting and informative booklet written by Matt Strickland (2006). It is aimed at '*young people who self-harm and those who care for them*'. It is quite colourful in its design and use of text to encouragement engagement by young people

http://www.suicidepreventionstudies.org/uploads/A%20Guide%20fo
r%20Young%20People.pdf

Martin, G., Hasking, P., Swannell, S., McAllister, M., Kay, T., (2010) *Seeking Solutions to Self-Injury: A Guide for Young People*, University of Queensland, Australia - This is quite a comprehensive booklet aimed again primarily at young people that offers a range of information, advice and some strategies that might be employed by individuals as a distraction from or way of coping with self-injury. It contains quite a comprehensive list of resources (including websites) at the end of the booklet.

Appendix One:

- **About CAPS and Collective Advocacy**

What is CAPS? :
CAPS is an independent advocacy organisation for people who use, or have used mental health services. CAPS works with mental health service users as individuals or as members of a group to set their own agenda, to find a stronger voice, to get their point across, and influence decisions which affect their lives.
We follow the principles of Independent Advocacy:
- Put the people who use advocacy first;
- Aim to be as free as possible from any conflicts of interest;
- Aim to be accountable to those we work with;
- Aim to be accessible to those we work with.

What is Collective Advocacy?
Collective advocacy supports people who use, or have used, mental health services by:
- Ensuring that people who use mental health services have an opportunity to have a say in the way that services are planned, provided and evaluated;
- Encouraging partnerships between service users and the people who plan, purchase and provide mental health services;
- Advocating for service user involvement in the training of doctors, social workers and other health professionals;
- Publishing service user perspectives on mental health issues;
- Being as accessible as possible, which includes using the arts and digital media to connect with people who might want to use advocacy.

Appendix Two:

- ### Online Survey

CAPS have heard from a writer and researcher Bruce Wallace from the University of Bedfordshire who has published an anthology of personal stories surrounding the struggle with self-injury. Bruce is now writing another book, about recovery and is interested in people's views and stories.

CAPS would like to consider contributing a collective voice to this book and if you feel you could help by giving us your views that would be very helpful. We are interested in all views and do not subscribe as an organization to any particular opinion or model. All contributions would be anonymous and we would show you what we have written and ask for your comments before anything was published.

If you would like to discuss this further please contact:

Naomi Salisbury

CAPS – The Consultation and Advocacy Service

Please try and keep yourself safe when answering the questionnaire. If you need to take a break or stop please do – support numbers will be included at the end of the survey.

Bruce says about the book he is preparing:

"Recovery is seen as a central and integral part of modern mental health practice; based around the recovery model and the idea of the individual having control (rather than the 'professional') together with a partnership rather than the practitioner/patient role

A different interpretation of recovery is based around the medical concept of becoming ill and needing treatment. After treatment the individual 'recovers'.

Neither of the above appear to sit comfortably within the realm of self-harm so individual's experiences and/or views on what recovery means or might mean becomes important. To date some individuals have indicated ideas such as recovery appears to be too finite a term when applied to self-harm unless the individual is confident that this is a past experience. Preference goes to terms such as 'in recovery'; 'recovering'."

- ***Please give us your views on the following questions:***

  - What would you like to say about self-harm and recovery?
  - Would you like CAPS to keep you updated about the results of this survey and to see what we have written based on people's views?

If so please leave your preferred contact details here - these will not be shared with any other organization.

Thank you very much for taking the time to give us your views.

If you would like to discuss the survey further please contact Naomi - Development Worker

If you would like to talk to someone right now here are some contact numbers and websites:

Samaritans
08457 90 90 90
www.samaritans.org/

Breathing Space
0800 838587
www.breathingspacescotland.co.uk

LifeSIGNS
www.lifesigns.org.uk/

National Self Harm Network
www.nshn.co.uk/

Appendix A:
B's Rules for Life:

1. Start the day with a SMILE!

A smile costs nothing, and helps to start the day on a positive. Keep smiling, and you may find it spreads to others.

2. Everyday have HUMAN CONTACT!

Human contact is good for you. It could be contact with a neighbour, or friends and family. It does you no good to hide away avoiding human contact.

3. Pay Attention! Look for the GOOD THINGS each and every day.

If you spend time looking, good and positive things can be found each and every day.

4. Be GENTLE WITH YOURSELF, and treat yourself with respect.

You treat **other** people with kindness and respect. You deserve to be treated **yourself** with kindness and respect.

5. Allow yourself to feel EMOTIONS.

Emotions are natural. Emotions are valuable to experience.

6. Remember that ALL THINGS WILL PASS.

All things will pass.

If you are unwell at the moment, be mindful that this, in time, will pass.

7. LIFE IS FOR LIVING.

Do not spend time fearing life. Get out there and live it. You only get one go!

8. Learn to RELAX AND HAVE FUN. You may enjoy it!

Relaxation and fun is good for you. It is important, and valuable. You cannot live your life constantly working.

9. Keep in touch with FRIENDS AND FAMILY.

Friends and family are important. They can share your problems, lend a hand, and be there for you. Friendships are too valuable to lose. After all, they chose to be your friend!

10. End the day thinking of the POSITIVES!

Do not end the day focusing on the bad things which have happened. Instead focus on the good and positive things.

Ingram Content Group UK Ltd.
Milton Keynes UK
UKHW011816170323
418736UK00001B/170